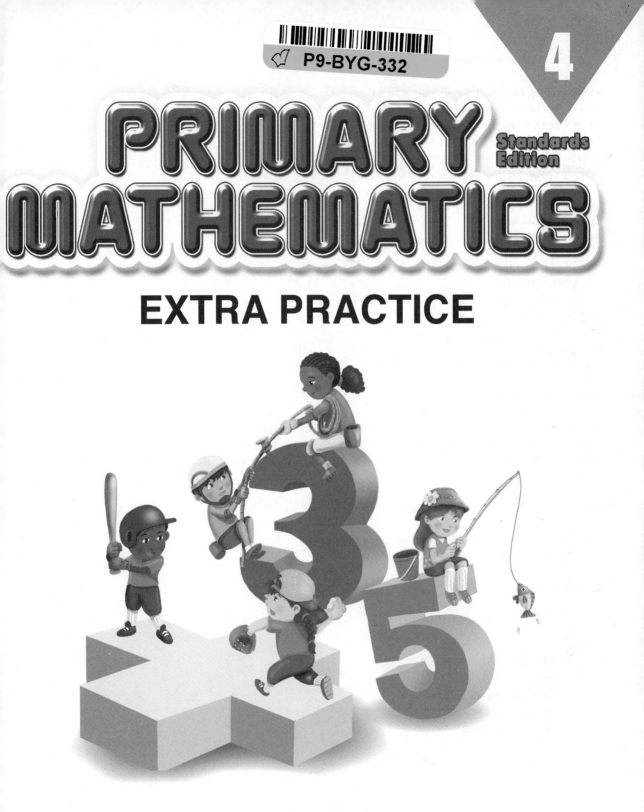

PRIMARY MATHEMATICS

Standards Edition

4

EXTRA PRACTICE

Lim Kian Chu

Marshall Cavendish
Education

SM
SingaporeMath.com Inc®

© 2008 Marshall Cavendish International (Singapore) Private Limited

Published by Marshall Cavendish Education
An imprint of Marshall Cavendish International (Singapore) Private Limited
Times Centre, 1 New Industrial Road, Singapore 536196
Customer Service Hotline: (65) 6411 0820
E-mail: tmesales@sg.marshallcavendish.com
Website: www.marshallcavendish.com/education

Marshall Cavendish Corporation
99 White Plains Road
Tarrytown, NY 10591
U.S.A.
Tel: (1-914) 332 8888
Fax: (1-914) 332 8882
E-mail: mcc@marshallcavendish.com
Website: www.marshallcavendish.com

First published 2008
Reprinted 2009, 2010, 2011, 2012 (twice), 2013

Primary Mathematics (Standards Edition) Extra Practice 4
ISBN: 978-0-7614-7005-2

Printed in Singapore

SingaporeMath.com Inc®
Distributed by
SingaporeMath.com Inc
404 Beavercreek Road #225
Oregon City, OR 97045
U.S.A.
Website: www.singaporemath.com

Preface

Primary Mathematics (Standards Edition) Extra Practice is a series of five supplementary books.

This series follows the topical arrangement in the Primary Mathematics (Standards Edition) Textbooks and Workbooks. Friendly Notes at the beginning of each unit provide a source for reference and revision of concepts. The level of difficulty, as well as the style of the problems, is similar to the exercises in the Textbooks and Workbooks. The short and topic-specific exercises enable instructors to assign work only in those topics in which the student needs more practice. This, together with the simple language used, allows students to review mathematics with minimal guidance.

Primary Mathematics (Standards Edition) Extra Practice aims to consolidate and reinforce the mathematical skills taught in the Primary Mathematics series. Students will master mathematical concepts with confidence through the use of this series.

Contents

Unit 1	**Whole Numbers**	**1**
Exercise 1	Ten Thousands, Hundred Thousands and Millions	7
Exercise 2	Approximation	11
Exercise 3	Factors	13
Exercise 4	Multiples	15
Exercise 5	Order of Operations	17
Exercise 6	Negative Numbers	19
Unit 2	**The Four Operations of Whole Numbers**	**21**
Exercise 1	Addition and Subtraction	23
Exercise 2	Multiplication and Division	25
Exercise 3	Multiplication by a 2-digit Number	27
Unit 3	**Fractions**	**29**
Exercise 1	Equivalent Fractions	35
Exercise 2	Adding and Subtracting Fractions	37
Exercise 3	Mixed Numbers	43
Exercise 4	Improper Fractions	45
Exercise 5	Fractions and Division	47
Exercise 6	Fraction of a Set	49
Unit 4	**Geometry**	**53**
Exercise 1	Right Angles	61
Exercise 2	Measuring Angles	63
Exercise 3	Perpendicular Lines	69
Exercise 4	Parallel Lines	71
Exercise 5	Quadrilaterals	73
Exercise 6	Triangles	75
Exercise 7	Circles	77
Exercise 8	Solid Figures	79
Exercise 9	Nets	81
Unit 5	**Area and Perimeter**	**83**
Exercise 1	Area of Rectangles	87
Exercise 2	Perimeter of Rectangles	89
Exercise 3	Composite Figures	91
Unit 6	**Decimals**	**95**
Exercise 1	Tenths	99
Exercise 2	Hundredths	101
Exercise 3	Thousandths	105
Exercise 4	Rounding	109

Unit 7	**The Four Operations of Decimals**	**111**
Exercise 1	Addition and Subtraction	115
Exercise 2	Multiplication	121
Exercise 3	Division	125
Unit 8	**Congruent and Symmetric Figures**	**131**
Exercise 1	Congruent Figures	135
Exercise 2	Tiling Patterns	137
Exercise 3	Line Symmetry	141
Exercise 4	Rotational Symmetry	145
Unit 9	**Coordinate Graphs and Changes in Quantities**	**147**
Exercise 1	The Coordinate Grid	149
Exercise 2	Changes in Quantities	151
Unit 10	**Data Analysis and Probability**	**153**
Exercise 1	Organizing and Analyzing Data	157
Exercise 2	Probability Experiments	159
Exercise 3	Order of Outcomes	161
Exercise 4	Bar Graphs	163
Exercise 5	Line Graphs	165
Unit 11	**Measures and Volume**	**167**
Exercise 1	Adding and Subtracting Measures	169
Exercise 2	Multiplying Measures	171
Exercise 3	Dividing Measures	175
Exercise 4	Cubic Units	179
Exercise 5	Volume of Rectangular Prisms	181
Answers		**183**

Blank

Unit 1 : Whole Numbers

Ten Thousands, Hundred Thousands and Millions

There are 5,382,746 people living in Country X. The place value of each digit in 5,382,746 is as follows:

Millions	Hundred thousands	Ten thousands	Thousands	Hundreds	Tens	Ones
5	3	8	2	7	4	6
5,000,000	300,000	80,000	2000	700	40	6

In 5,382,746

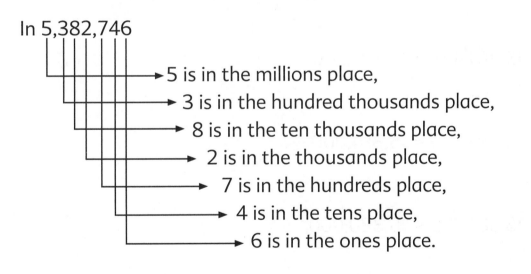

5 is in the millions place,

3 is in the hundred thousands place,

8 is in the ten thousands place,

2 is in the thousands place,

7 is in the hundreds place,

4 is in the tens place,

6 is in the ones place.

We write 5,382,746 in words as five million, three hundred eighty-two thousand, seven hundred forty-six.

5,382,746 is the **standard form**.

5,000,000 + 300,000 + 80,000 + 2000 + 700 + 40 + 6 is the **expanded form** of 5,382,746.

1

Approximation

When we round up or round down values, these rounded values are only **approximations**. We use the symbol '≈' to show approximation. '≈' means 'is approximately to'.
To round a number to a certain place value, we look at the digit in the next lower place value.
If the digit is 0, 1, 2, 3 or 4, we round down. If it is 5, 6, 7, 8 or 9, we round up.

Round 15,381,479 to the nearest

(a) ten,   (b) hundred,   (c) thousand,
(d) ten thousand,   (e) hundred thousand,   (f) million.

(a) 15,381,479 ≈ 15,381,480

(b) 15,381,479 ≈ 15,381,500

(c) 15,381,479 ≈ 15,381,000

(d) 15,381,479 ≈ 15,380,000

(e) 15,381,479 ≈ 15,400,000

(f) 15,381,479 ≈ 15,000,000

Primary Mathematics (Standards Edition) Extra Practice 4   © 2008 Marshall Cavendish International (Singapore) Private Limited

Factors

Factor × Factor = Product

20 is the product of 4 and 5.

4 × 5 = 20
4 and 5 are factors of 20.

1 × 20 = 20
2 × 10 = 20

The number 20 has 6 factors.
1, 2, 4, 5, 10 and 20.

1, 2, 10 and 20 are also factors of 20.

Some numbers have exactly 2 factors.

A number greater than 1 is called a **prime number** if it has exactly **two factors**, 1 and the number itself.

1 × 3 = 3, 1 × 5 = 5, 1 × 7 = 7, ...
3, 5, 7, ... are prime numbers.

A number greater than 1 is a **composite number** if it has more than two factors.

The number 1 is not a prime number or a composite number.

1 × 4 = 4, 2 × 2 = 4
The factors of 4 are 1, 2 and 4.
Therefore, 4 is a composite number.

Multiples

The table shows the first ten multiples of 2, 3, 4, 5, 6, 7, 8, 9 and 10.

×										
	2	4	6	8	10	12	14	16	18	20
	3	6	9	12	15	18	21	(24)	27	30
	4	8	12	16	20	(24)	28	32	36	40
	5	10	15	20	25	30	35	40	45	50
	6	12	18	24	30	36	42	(48)	54	60
	7	14	21	28	35	42	49	56	63	70
	8	16	24	32	40	(48)	56	64	72	80
	9	18	27	36	45	54	63	72	81	90
	10	20	30	40	50	60	70	80	90	100

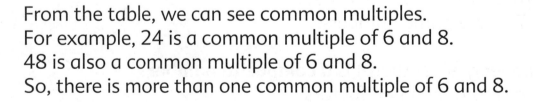

8 is a multiple of 2.
2 is a factor of 8.

8 is a multiple of 4.
4 is a factor of 8.

From the table, we can see common multiples.
For example, 24 is a common multiple of 6 and 8.
48 is also a common multiple of 6 and 8.
So, there is more than one common multiple of 6 and 8.

6 and 8 are factors of 24 and 48.

Primary Mathematics (Standards Edition) Extra Practice 4

© 2008 Marshall Cavendish International (Singapore) Private Limited

Order of Operations

An expression has numbers and operation signs (+, −, ×, ÷) but no equal sign.
An equation is a number sentence with an equal sign.
The value on each side of the equal sign is the same.

When an expression involves different operation signs and parentheses, we proceed as follows:
- Do what is in the parentheses first.
- Next, carry out multiplication or division from left to right.
- Then carry out addition or subtraction from left to right.

1. Find the value of $18 + 32 \div 4 - 5$.

$$18 + 32 \div 4 - 5 = 18 + 8 - 5$$
$$= 26 - 5$$
$$= 21$$

$18 + 32 \div 4 - 5$
$\underbrace{}_{8}$
$= 18 + \underbrace{8 - 5}_{26}$
$= 26 - 5$
$= 21$

2. Find the value of $32 + (16 - 2) \times (4 \div 2)$.

$$32 + (16 - 2) \times (4 \div 2) = 32 + \underbrace{14 \times 2}_{28}$$
$$= 32 + 28$$
$$= 60$$

Negative Numbers

A number with a negative sign in front of it is known as a **negative number**.

The negative sign is also used as a symbol for subtraction.

On the number line, the positive numbers are to the right of zero. The negative numbers are to the left of zero.

On the number line, '−3' is on the left of '−2' and '−1' is on the right of '−2'. We note that −3 < −2,
−2 < −1,
−2 > −3 and
−1 > −2.

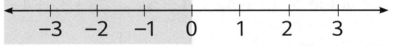

Examples of use of negative numbers in our daily life include the following:

1. Temperatures below 0 °C

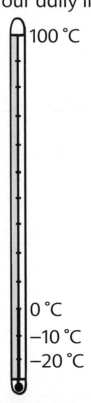

2. Depths below sea level

Exercise 1 : Ten Thousands, Hundred Thousands and Millions

1. Write the following in standard form.

   (a) 27 thousands 5 ones   _____

   (b) 250 thousands 6 hundreds   _____

   (c) 90,000 + 3000 + 9   _____

   (d) 500,000 + 50,000 + 40 + 6   _____

2. Write the following in expanded form.

   (a) forty-seven thousand, five hundred

   _____

   (b) five hundred sixteen thousand, two hundred forty

   _____

   (c) six hundred two thousand, eighty-three

   _____

   (d) ninety-three thousand, five

   _____

   (e) two million, one hundred thirty thousand

   _____

   (f) eight million, fifteen thousand

   _____

3. Write the following in words.

   (a) 40,516

   _____

   (b) 10,020

   _____

   (c) 213,400

   _____

   (d) 502,001

   _____

   (e) 300,208

   _____

   (f) 5,006,000

   _____

   (g) 348,715,908

   _____

4. Fill in the blanks.

   (a) In 32,105, the digit 1 stands for _____.

   (b) In 43,027, the digit 3 is in the _____ place,
       its value is _____.

   (c) In 123,456, the digit 2 is in the _____ place,
       its value is _____.

Primary Mathematics (Standards Edition) Extra Practice 4   © 2008 Marshall Cavendish International (Singapore) Private Limited

(d) In 240,170, the digit 2 stands for _____.

(e) In 5,300,000, the value of 5 is _____.

(f) In 21,643,708, the hundreds digit is _____
and the ten millions digit is _____.

5. Fill in the blanks.

(a) 30,000 + 5000 + 200 + 6 = _____

(b) 428,000 + 7 = _____

(c) 81,690 = 81,000 + _____ + 90

(d) 573,012 = 500,000 + _____ + 3000 + 10 + 2

6. Fill in the blanks.

(a) _____ is 1000 less than 50,326.

(b) There are _____ hundreds in 60,000.

(c) _____ is 1000 less than 172,000.

(d) _____ is 10,000 more than 1,341,979.

7. Complete the following regular number patterns.
(a) 25,702, 25,732 , 25,762, _____ , _____

(b) 40,036, _____ , _____ , 40,336, 40,436

(c) 69,271, _____ , 71,271, 72,271, _____

(d) 55,810, 60,810, _____ , _____ , 75,810

8. Arrange the numbers in increasing order.
   (a) 16,538,   46,385,   336,058,   130,568

   _____

   (b) 140,105,   104,002,   23,806,441,   1,165,305

   _____

9. Fill in the boxes.
   (a) 26,540,189 = ☐ ten millions + ☐ millions

   + ☐ hundred thousands

   + ☐ ten thousands

   + ☐ thousands

   + ☐ hundred

   + ☐ tens

   + ☐ ones

   (b) 253,704,986 = ☐ ones + ☐ hundreds

   + ☐ millions

   + ☐ hundred millions

   + ☐ thousands

   + ☐ ten thousands

   + ☐ tens

   + ☐ ten millions

   + ☐ hundred thousands

Primary Mathematics (Standards Edition) Extra Practice 4

Exercise 2 : Approximation

1. Round each number to the nearest ten.

    (a) 566 _____   (b) 1285 _____

    (c) 12,403 _____   (d) 107,412 _____

2. Round each number to the nearest hundred.

    (a) 4853 _____   (b) 11,864 _____

    (c) 318,009 _____   (d) 1,564,050 _____

3. Round each number to the nearest thousand.

    (a) 21,647 _____   (b) 107,014 _____

    (c) 741,806 _____   (d) 23,785,491 _____

4. Round each number to the nearest ten thousand.

    (a) 17,496 _____   (b) 289,099 _____

    (c) 1,452,647 _____ (d) 106,472,854 _____

5. Round each number to the nearest hundred thousand.

    (a) 146,522 _____   (b) 7,210,547 _____

    (c) 19,545,371 _____ (d) 124,751,802 _____

6. Round each number to the nearest million.

   (a) 2,950,000 _____

   (b) 17,814,090 _____

   (c) 389,546,713 _____

   (d) 539,014,000 _____

7. The price of a house is $1,760,800.
   Round the price to the nearest hundred thousand.

   _____

8. A fast food restaurant sold 28,726,481 burgers in a year.
   Round the figure to the nearest million.

   _____

Primary Mathematics (Standards Edition) Extra Practice 4

© 2008 Marshall Cavendish International (Singapore) Private Limited

Exercise 3 : Factors

1. Fill in the missing factors.

   (a) $42 = 6 \times \boxed{}$ (b) $9 \times \boxed{} = 72$

   (c) $90 = 5 \times \boxed{}$ (d) $100 = \boxed{} \times 4$

2. Find the factors of each number.

   (a) 18   (b) 81

   The factors of 18 are   The factors of 81 are

   _____.   _____.

   (c) 56   (d) 98

   The factors of 56 are   The factors of 98 are

   _____.   _____.

3. Answer the questions using the numbers below.

36   12   20   27   11   19

Which of the above numbers have each of the following as factors?

(a) 2 _____

(b) 3 _____

(c) 5 _____

(d) Which of the above numbers are prime numbers?

_____

(e) Which of the above numbers are composite numbers?

_____

4. Write a number in each ☐ to make the number sentence true.

(a) $12 \times 2 = 2 \times \boxed{} \times 3$

(b) $12 \times 4 = \boxed{} \times 8 \times 2$

(c) $6 \times 14 = 7 \times \boxed{}$

(d) $35 \times 36 = 35 \times \boxed{} \times 4$

5. Answer these questions. Show all your work clearly.

(a) Is 6 a common factor of 84 and 90?

(b) What are the common factors of 12 and 18?

Primary Mathematics (Standards Edition) Extra Practice 4
© 2008 Marshall Cavendish International (Singapore) Private Limited

Exercise 4 : Multiples

1. List the first four multiples of each number.

    (a) 3   (b) 5

    The first four   The first four
    multiples of 3 are   multiples of 5 are

    _____.   _____.

    (c) 7   (d) 9

    The first four   The first four
    multiples of 7 are   multiples of 9 are

    _____.   _____.

2. Find the first two common multiples of each set of numbers.

    (a) 6 and 9

    (b) 3, 4 and 6

3. Use the numbers below to answer the questions.

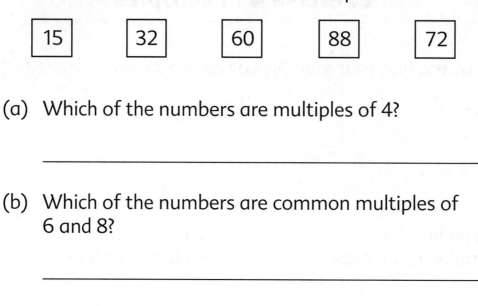

| 15 | 32 | 60 | 88 | 72 |

(a) Which of the numbers are multiples of 4?

_____

(b) Which of the numbers are common multiples of 6 and 8?

_____

4. (a) What is the fifth multiple of 12?

_____

(b) What is the eighth multiple of 15?

_____

5. Complete the regular number patterns.

(a) 15, 30, 45, _____, _____, 90

(b) 9, 18, _____, _____, _____, 54

Primary Mathematics (Standards Edition) Extra Practice 4

Exercise 5 : Order of Operations

1. Find the value of the following.

(a) $20 - 8 + 6$	(b) $121 + 2 - 65$
(c) $3 \times 4 - 6$	(d) $7 \times 8 \div 4$
(e) $80 - 30 \div 5 \times 9$	(f) $115 + 8 \times 6 \div 6$
(g) $218 + (36 - 12) \div 2$	(h) $108 - (99 \div 9) \times 4$

2. Do these. Show all your work clearly.

(a) There are 25 apples and 15 pears in one box.
There are 4 such boxes of fruits.
How many more apples than pears are there in all?

(b) George bought 2 hamburgers and 3 cheeseburgers.
Each hamburger cost $1.60. Each cheeseburger cost
$1.35. Find the total amount George had to pay.

Primary Mathematics (Standards Edition) Extra Practice 4

Exercise 6 : Negative Numbers

1. Use the number line to answer the questions.

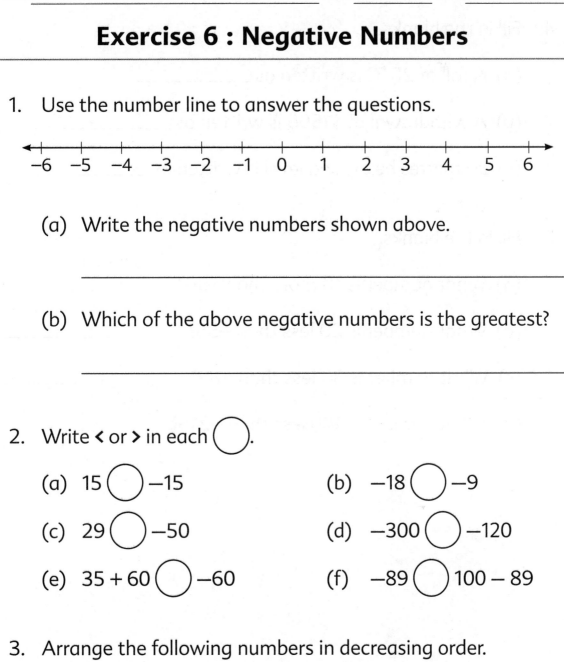

(a) Write the negative numbers shown above.

_____

(b) Which of the above negative numbers is the greatest?

_____

2. Write **<** or **>** in each ◯.

(a) 15 ◯ −15

(b) −18 ◯ −9

(c) 29 ◯ −50

(d) −300 ◯ −120

(e) 35 + 60 ◯ −60

(f) −89 ◯ 100 − 89

3. Arrange the following numbers in decreasing order.

28,   −91,   100,   −66,   −19

_____

Primary Mathematics (Standards Edition) Extra Practice 4

4. Fill in the blanks.

(a) A fall of 20 °C is written as _____.

(b) A withdrawal of $1500 is written as _____.

(c) 20 metres below sea level is written as _____.

5. Fill in the blanks.

(a) What number is 10 more than −30?   _____

(b) What number is 20 less than −55?   _____

(c) What number is 30 less than −82?   _____

(d) What number is 100 less than −215?   _____

Primary Mathematics (Standards Edition) Extra Practice 4   © 2008 Marshall Cavendish International (Singapore) Private Limited

Unit 2 : The Four Operations of Whole Numbers

Friendly Notes

Addition and Subtraction

When we add two or more numbers, we get their **sum**.
When we subtract two or more numbers, we find their **difference**.
We can draw models to help us with addition and subtraction.

Joni has 1228 seashells.
Her sister has 346 fewer seashells than Joni.

(a) How many seashells does Joni's sister have?
(b) How many seashells do they have altogether?

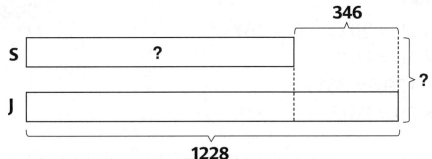

(a) $1228 - 346 = 882$

Joni's sister has 882 seashells.

(b) $1228 + 882 = 2110$

They have 2110 seashells altogether.

Primary Mathematics (Standards Edition) Extra Practice 4

Multiplication and Division

When we multiply two or more numbers, we find their **product**.
When a number is divided by another number exactly, the answer is the **quotient**.
When a number is not exactly divided by another number, the answer is the quotient and the **remainder**.

We can multiply a 3-digit number by a 2-digit number as follows:

1. Find the product of 297 and 29.

   Method 1:

   ```
        2 9 7
    ×     2 9
     ─────────
      2 6 7 3
      5 9 4 0
     ─────────
      8 6 1 3
   ```

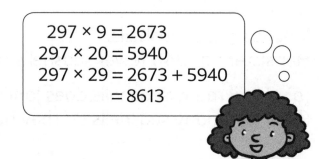

$297 \times 9 = 2673$
$297 \times 20 = 5940$
$297 \times 29 = 2673 + 5940$
$\qquad\qquad = 8613$

   Method 2:

   $297 \times 29 = 297 \times 30 - 297$
   $297 \times 30 = 8910$
   $8910 - 297 = 8613$
   $297 \times 29 = 8613$

We can divide a 4-digit number by another number as follows:

2. Find the value of $3468 \div 6$.

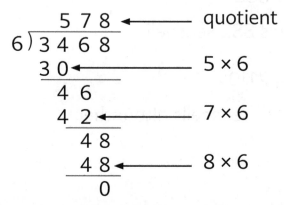

5×6

7×6

8×6

quotient

Primary Mathematics (Standards Edition) Extra Practice 4   © 2008 Marshall Cavendish International (Singapore) Private Limited

Exercise 1 : Addition and Subtraction

1. Find the sum of the following numbers.

   (a) $909 + 1826$

   (b) $2647 + 13{,}121$

   (c) $812{,}346 + 2{,}214{,}718$

   (d) $20{,}146{,}119 + 2004$

2. Find the difference between the numbers.

   (a) $98{,}147 - 45{,}725$

   (b) $16{,}032{,}518 - 8{,}147{,}622$

   (c) $23{,}114{,}278 - 1364$

   (d) $123{,}146{,}283 - 20{,}102{,}460$

3. Fill in the blanks.

   (a) What number must be added to 950 to get 1500?

   _____

   (b) What number must be subtracted from 2568 to get 1005?

   _____

4. Do these. Show all your work clearly.

   (a) Liza has 106 dolls. Jean has 29 fewer dolls than Liza.
       How many dolls do they have altogether?

   (b) There were 8645 people at an airport.
       There were 3728 men and 2144 women.
       The rest were children.
       How many more children were there than women?

Primary Mathematics (Standards Edition) Extra Practice 4

Name: _____ Class: _____ Date: _____

Exercise 2 : Multiplication and Division

1. Multiply.

   (a) $67 \times 8 =$ 　　　　　　　　　(b) $705 \times 6 =$

   (c) $6879 \times 8 =$ 　　　　　　　　(d) $5068 \times 4 =$

2. Divide.

   (a) $392 \div 7 =$ 　　　　　　　　　(b) $7248 \div 8 =$

   (c) $4428 \div 6 =$ 　　　　　　　　(d) $5067 \div 9 =$

3. Do these. Show all your work clearly.

(a) 8912 adults visited a book fair.
There were thrice as many children as adults.
How many children were there?

(b) Janson has 966 stamps.
He gives them equally to 6 friends.
How many stamps does each friend get?

Primary Mathematics (Standards Edition) Extra Practice 4

Exercise 3 : Multiplication by a 2-digit Number

1. Find the product of each pair of numbers.
   (a) 72 and 70   (b) 568 and 90

   (c) 69 and 28   (d) 800 and 50

   (e) 98 and 637   (f) 509 and 46

2. Estimate and then multiply.
   (a) 68 × 27   (b) 946 × 42

3. Do these. Show all your work clearly.

   (a) A guava weighs 385 g. It is 10 times as light as a watermelon. What is the total weight of the two fruits?

   (b) There are 36 boys and 43 girls in a reading club. If each boy reads 8 books and each girl reads 12 books, how many books will they read altogether?

Unit 3 : Fractions

Friendly Notes

Equivalent Fractions

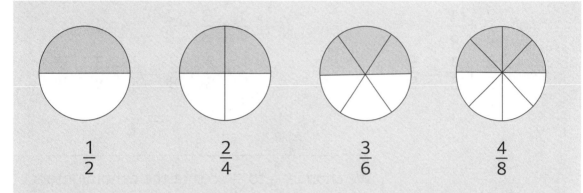

$$\frac{1}{2} \qquad \frac{2}{4} \qquad \frac{3}{6} \qquad \frac{4}{8}$$

We can see that the size of each circle is the same.

We notice that half of each circle is shaded.

So, $\frac{1}{2} = \frac{2}{4} = \frac{3}{6} = \frac{4}{8}$.

$\frac{1}{2}$, $\frac{2}{4}$, $\frac{3}{6}$ and $\frac{4}{8}$ are called **equivalent fractions**.

$\frac{1}{2}$ is a fraction in its **simplest form**.

All the other fractions are $\frac{1}{2}$ when reduced to their simplest forms.

Name two equivalent fractions of $\frac{4}{12}$.

$$\frac{4}{12} \begin{array}{c} \div 4 \\ \div 4 \end{array} = \frac{1}{3}$$

$$\frac{4}{12} \begin{array}{c} \times 2 \\ \times 2 \end{array} = \frac{8}{24}$$

We can divide or multiply the numerator and the denominator by the same number to get equivalent fractions.

Adding and Subtracting Fractions

We can only add or subtract fractions when their denominators are the same.

1. Add.

(a) $\frac{2}{5} + \frac{1}{5} = \frac{3}{5}$

$\frac{2}{5} + \frac{1}{5} = \frac{3}{5}$

(b) $\frac{1}{4} + \frac{3}{8} + \frac{2}{8} \quad \frac{7}{8}$

$\frac{1}{4} + \frac{3}{8} + \frac{2}{8} = \frac{2}{8} + \frac{3}{8} + \frac{2}{8}$

$\frac{2}{8}, \frac{3}{8}, \frac{2}{8}$

$= \frac{7}{8}$

We change $\frac{1}{4}$ to $\frac{2}{8}$ so that the denominators are the same and we can add the numerators.

2. Subtract.

(a) $\frac{5}{6} - \frac{1}{6} \quad \frac{4}{6}$

$\frac{5}{6} - \frac{2}{6} = \frac{3}{6}$

$= \frac{1}{2}$

(b) $1 - \frac{5}{12} - \frac{2}{12}$

$1 - \frac{5}{12} - \frac{2}{12} = \frac{12}{12} - \frac{5}{12} - \frac{2}{12}$

$= \frac{5}{12}$

We change one whole to $\frac{12}{12}$ before we subtract.

Write your answer in its simplest form.

Primary Mathematics (Standards Edition) Extra Practice 4

Mixed Numbers

We get a **mixed number** when we add a whole number and a fraction.

$5\frac{1}{3}$, $6\frac{3}{7}$ and $8\frac{3}{8}$ are mixed numbers.

1. Write a mixed number.

   (a)

   $= 2\frac{1}{2}$

   (b) 6 wholes 5 sevenths $= 6\frac{5}{7}$

2. Find the value of the following.

   (a) $7 + \frac{3}{4}$ $\subset$ $7\frac{3}{4}$

   $7 + \frac{3}{4} = 7\frac{3}{4}$

   (b) $9 - \frac{1}{3}$

   $9 - \frac{1}{3} = 8\frac{3}{3} - \frac{1}{3}$

   $= 8\frac{2}{3}$

Improper Fractions

In an **improper fraction**, the numerator is greater than or equal to its denominator.
Improper fractions are equal to or greater than 1.
We can express an improper fraction as a whole number or a mixed number.

1. Circle the improper fractions.

$\frac{1}{2}$, $\left(\frac{5}{5}\right)$ $\frac{2}{4}$, $\left(\frac{6}{5}\right)$ $\left(\frac{9}{8}\right)$ $\left(\frac{1}{1}\right)$

2. Change the improper fraction $\frac{9}{4}$ to a mixed number.

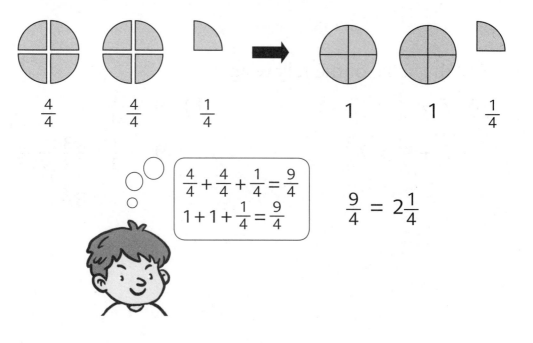

$$\frac{4}{4} + \frac{4}{4} + \frac{1}{4} = \frac{9}{4}$$
$$1 + 1 + \frac{1}{4} = \frac{9}{4}$$

$$\frac{9}{4} = 2\frac{1}{4}$$

Primary Mathematics (Standards Edition) Extra Practice 4

Fractions and Division

Share 5 pizzas equally among 4 children.

Method 1

$$5 \div 4 = \frac{5}{4}$$
$$= \frac{4}{4} + \frac{1}{4}$$
$$= 1\frac{1}{4}$$

The remaining whole is divided into 4 parts. Each child gets $\frac{1}{4}$ of this pizza. Altogether, each child gets $1\frac{1}{4}$ pizzas.

Method 2

$$5 \div 4 = 1\frac{1}{4}$$

$$\begin{array}{r} 1 \\ 4\overline{)\,5} \\ 4 \\ \hline 1 \end{array}$$

Primary Mathematics (Standards Edition) Extra Practice 4

Fraction of a Set

1. This is a set of fruits.
   What fraction of the set of fruits are mangoes?

   4 mangoes   4 oranges   4 apples   4 pears

   There are 16 fruits in the set. 4 of the fruits are mangoes.

   $$\frac{4}{16} = \frac{1}{4}$$

   Write $\frac{4}{16}$ in its simplest form.

   $\frac{1}{4}$ of the fruits are mangoes.

   $\frac{1}{5}$ {
   $\frac{1}{5}$ {
   $\frac{1}{5}$ {
   $\frac{1}{5}$ {

   4 equal parts

2. (a) How many apples does each child get?
   There are 20 apples. There are 5 children.

   $$\frac{1}{5} \text{ of } 20 = \frac{1}{5} \times 20 = \frac{20}{5}$$
   $$= 4$$

   What is $\frac{1}{5}$ of 20?

   Each child gets 4 apples.

   (b) What is $\frac{2}{5}$ of 20?
   $$\frac{2}{5} \text{ of } 20 = \frac{2}{5} \times 20 = \frac{40}{5}$$
   $$= 8$$

   Two children get 8 apples altogether.

Primary Mathematics (Standards Edition) Extra Practice 4

Exercise 1 : Equivalent Fractions

1. Find the missing numerators.

   (a) $\dfrac{1}{4} = \dfrac{2}{8}$

   (b) $\dfrac{2}{5} = \dfrac{4}{10}$

   (c) $\dfrac{5}{6} = \dfrac{15}{18}$

   (d) $\dfrac{3}{8} = \dfrac{9}{24}$

   (e) $\dfrac{1}{2} = \dfrac{10}{20}$

   (f) $\dfrac{7}{9} = \dfrac{28}{36}$

2. Find the missing denominators.

   (a) $\dfrac{1}{3} = \dfrac{3}{9}$

   (b) $\dfrac{2}{3} = \dfrac{4}{6}$

   (c) $\dfrac{3}{4} = \dfrac{9}{12}$

   (d) $\dfrac{10}{25} = \dfrac{2}{5}$

   (e) $\dfrac{24}{30} = \dfrac{4}{5}$

   (f) $\dfrac{20}{28} = \dfrac{5}{7}$

3. Complete these equivalent fractions.

   (a) $\dfrac{1}{2} = \dfrac{3}{6} = \dfrac{6}{12} = \dfrac{9}{18}$

   (b) $\dfrac{3}{5} = \dfrac{9}{15} = \dfrac{15}{25} = \dfrac{24}{40}$

$\dfrac{4}{5} = \dfrac{24}{30}$

$\dfrac{3}{5} = \dfrac{24}{40}$

Primary Mathematics (Standards Edition) Extra Practice 4

4. Express each of the following fractions in its simplest form.

   (a) $\frac{6}{8} = \frac{3}{4}$

   (b) $\frac{5}{20} = $

   (c) $\frac{18}{27} = $

   (d) $\frac{10}{15} = $

5. Arrange the fractions in increasing order.

   (a) $\frac{10}{20}, \frac{4}{5}, \frac{7}{10}$ _____

   (b) $\frac{5}{6}, \frac{2}{3}, \frac{9}{12}$ _____

6. Arrange the fractions in decreasing order.

   (a) $\frac{2}{3}, \frac{5}{6}, \frac{5}{9}$ _____

   (b) $\frac{1}{2}, \frac{5}{6}, \frac{3}{4}$ _____

7. Do these. Show all your work clearly.

   (a) Cameron drank $\frac{5}{8}$ ℓ of water. Dani drank $\frac{4}{5}$ ℓ of water. Who drank more?

   (b) A pumpkin weighs $\frac{4}{5}$ kg. A melon weighs $\frac{9}{10}$ kg. A papaya weighs $\frac{13}{20}$ kg. Which is the heaviest? Which is the lightest?

Primary Mathematics (Standards Edition) Extra Practice 4

Exercise 2 : Adding and Subtracting Fractions

1. Add. Write the answers in the simplest form.

(a) $\frac{1}{5} + \frac{1}{5}$ $= \frac{2}{5}$	(b) $\frac{2}{7} + \frac{3}{7}$ $= \frac{5}{7}$	(c) $\frac{7}{10} + \frac{1}{10}$ $=$
(d) $\frac{4}{12} + \frac{4}{12}$ $=$	(e) $\frac{2}{9} + \frac{5}{9}$ $=$	(f) $\frac{1}{2} + \frac{1}{2}$ $=$

2. Write the missing numbers.

(a) $\frac{1}{6} + \frac{1}{3}$

$= \frac{1}{6} + \square$

$= \square$

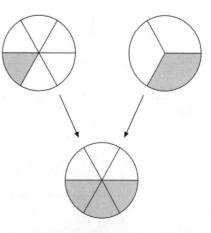

(b) $\frac{3}{4} + \frac{1}{8}$

$= \boxed{} + \frac{1}{8}$

$= \boxed{}$

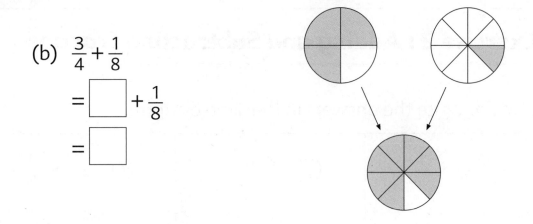

3. Add. Write the answers in the simplest form.

(a) $\frac{1}{4} + \frac{1}{4} + \frac{1}{4} =$ $3\frac{1}{4}$	(b) $\frac{2}{6} + \frac{1}{6} + \frac{2}{6} =$
(c) $\frac{2}{8} + \frac{3}{8} + \frac{1}{8} =$	(d) $\frac{1}{3} + \frac{1}{3} + \frac{1}{3} =$
(e) $\frac{5}{10} + \frac{3}{10} + \frac{2}{10} =$ 1	(f) $\frac{1}{12} + \frac{7}{12} + \frac{2}{12} =$

4. Add. Write the answers in the simplest form.

(a) $\frac{1}{5} + \frac{3}{10}$ $=$	(b) $\frac{1}{3} + \frac{2}{6}$ $=$	(c) $\frac{1}{10} + \frac{1}{2}$ $=$
(d) $\frac{5}{12} + \frac{1}{3}$ $=$	(e) $\frac{2}{4} + \frac{2}{8}$ $=$	(f) $\frac{3}{4} + \frac{2}{12}$ $=$

Primary Mathematics (Standards Edition) Extra Practice 4

5. Subtract.

(a)

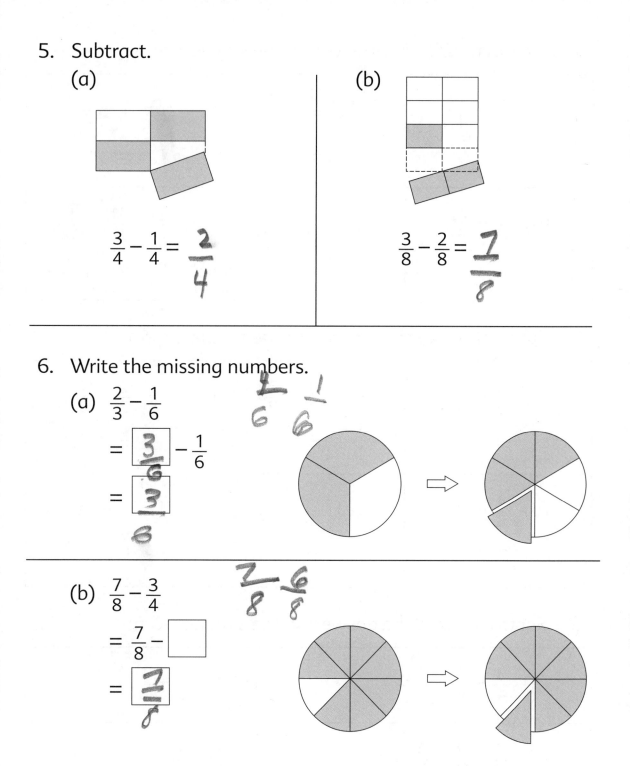

$$\frac{3}{4} - \frac{1}{4} = \frac{2}{4}$$

(b)

$$\frac{3}{8} - \frac{2}{8} = \frac{7}{8}$$

6. Write the missing numbers.

(a) $\frac{2}{3} - \frac{1}{6}$

$$= \boxed{\frac{3}{6}} - \frac{1}{6}$$

$$= \boxed{\frac{3}{6}}$$

(b) $\frac{7}{8} - \frac{3}{4}$

$$= \frac{7}{8} - \boxed{}$$

$$= \boxed{\frac{1}{8}}$$

Primary Mathematics (Standards Edition) Extra Practice 4

7. Subtract. Write the answers in the simplest form.

(a) $\dfrac{3}{4} - \dfrac{1}{4}$ =	(b) $\dfrac{4}{5} - \dfrac{2}{5}$ =	(c) $1 - \dfrac{4}{7}$ =
(d) $\dfrac{7}{9} - \dfrac{4}{9}$ =	(e) $\dfrac{8}{10} - \dfrac{6}{10}$ =	(f) $\dfrac{11}{12} - \dfrac{9}{12}$ =

8. Subtract. Write the answers in the simplest form.

(a) $\dfrac{5}{6} - \dfrac{2}{3}$ =	(b) $\dfrac{3}{4} - \dfrac{2}{8}$ =	(c) $\dfrac{2}{3} - \dfrac{1}{9}$ =
(d) $\dfrac{4}{5} - \dfrac{3}{10}$ =	(e) $\dfrac{7}{12} - \dfrac{1}{3}$ =	(f) $1 - \dfrac{2}{10}$ =

9. Subtract. Write the answers in the simplest form.

(a) $\dfrac{3}{4} - \dfrac{1}{4} - \dfrac{1}{4} =$	(b) $1 - \dfrac{3}{5} - \dfrac{1}{5} =$
(c) $\dfrac{5}{7} - \dfrac{2}{7} - \dfrac{3}{7} =$	(d) $\dfrac{8}{9} - \dfrac{4}{9} - \dfrac{1}{9} =$
(e) $\dfrac{7}{10} - \dfrac{3}{10} - \dfrac{2}{10} =$	(f) $1 - \dfrac{2}{12} - \dfrac{4}{12} =$

Primary Mathematics (Standards Edition) Extra Practice 4

10. Do these. Show all your work clearly.

   (a) Mary walked $\frac{4}{7}$ of the journey to the library.
   What fraction of the journey did she still have to walk?

   (b) A piece of cloth is $\frac{3}{8}$ ft long.
   Another piece of cloth is $\frac{1}{4}$ ft long.
   What is the total length of the 2 pieces of cloth?

   (c) Andrew and John shared a pizza.
   Andrew ate $\frac{1}{12}$ of the pizza and John ate $\frac{1}{3}$ of it.
   Who ate more? How much more did he eat?

(d) Ann ate $\frac{1}{4}$ of a cake.

Dylan ate $\frac{1}{4}$ of the cake more than Ann.

What fraction of the cake did they eat altogether?

(e) Susan had 1 kg of sugar.

After she had used $\frac{2}{5}$ kg, Janice gave her another $\frac{1}{10}$ kg of sugar. How much sugar did Susan have after that?

Exercise 3 : Mixed Numbers

1. Write a mixed number for each of the following.

   (a) 2 wholes 1 half = _____

   (b) 3 wholes 2 thirds = _____

   (c) 2 wholes 3 quarters = _____

   (d) 7 wholes 5 eighths = _____

2. Find the value of each of the following.

   (a) $2 + \dfrac{7}{8} =$ _____   (b) $\dfrac{3}{4} + 3 =$ _____

   (c) $2 - \dfrac{2}{3} =$ _____   (d) $5 - \dfrac{2}{5} =$ _____

3. Add or subtract. Give each answer in its simplest form.

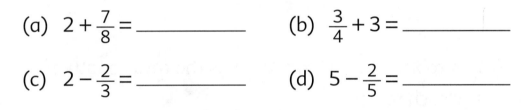

   (a) $\dfrac{7}{10} + \dfrac{5}{10} =$ $\dfrac{12}{10} = \dfrac{6}{5}$ (b) $2\dfrac{5}{8} + \dfrac{7}{8} =$ _____

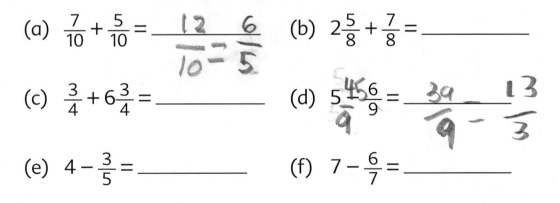

   (c) $\dfrac{3}{4} + 6\dfrac{3}{4} =$ _____   (d) $5\dfrac{4\,5\,6}{9} = \dfrac{39}{9} - \dfrac{13}{3}$

   (e) $4 - \dfrac{3}{5} =$ _____   (f) $7 - \dfrac{6}{7} =$ _____

43

4. Do these. Show all your work clearly.

(a) A string 28 yd long is cut into 10 equal pieces. What is the length of each piece?

(b) A table is $1\frac{1}{2}$ m long. What is the total length of 3 such tables?

Primary Mathematics (Standards Edition) Extra Practice 4

© 2008 Marshall Cavendish International (Singapore) Private Limited

Exercise 4 : Improper Fractions

1. Write the improper fraction for each of the following.

   (a) 10 fifths = $\frac{10}{5}$

   (b) 9 quarters = _____

   (c) 18 sixths = _____

   (d) 11 thirds = _____

2. Find the missing numerator in each of the following.

   (a) $2 = \frac{\square}{6}$

   (b) $5 = \frac{\square}{2}$

   (c) $2\frac{3}{4} = 1\frac{\square}{4}$

   (d) $3\frac{2}{5} = 2\frac{7}{5}$

   (e) $4\frac{2}{3} = 3\frac{\square}{3}$

   (f) $5\frac{5}{6} = 4\frac{\square}{6}$

3. Change each improper fraction to a mixed number or a whole number.

   (a) $\frac{9}{5} =$ $1\frac{4}{5}$

   (b) $\frac{18}{6} =$ 3

   (c) $\frac{15}{4} =$ _____

   (d) $\frac{19}{10} =$ _____

4. Express each of the following as a whole number or a mixed number in its simplest form.

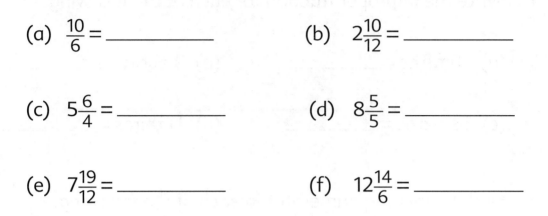

(a) $\dfrac{10}{6} =$ _____

(b) $2\dfrac{10}{12} =$ _____

(c) $5\dfrac{6}{4} =$ _____

(d) $8\dfrac{5}{5} =$ _____

(e) $7\dfrac{19}{12} =$ _____

(f) $12\dfrac{14}{6} =$ _____

5. Express each mixed number as an improper fraction.

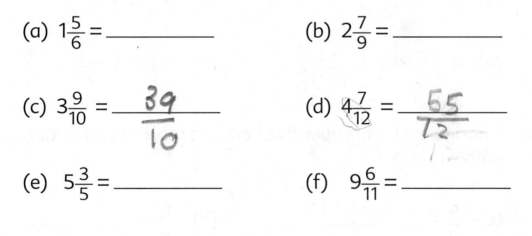

(a) $1\dfrac{5}{6} =$ _____

(b) $2\dfrac{7}{9} =$ _____

(c) $3\dfrac{9}{10} = \dfrac{39}{10}$

(d) $4\dfrac{7}{12} = \dfrac{55}{12}$

(e) $5\dfrac{3}{5} =$ _____

(f) $9\dfrac{6}{11} =$ _____

Exercise 5 : Fractions and Division

1. Fill in the blanks.
    Share 6 pizzas equally among 4 children.

    _M/6_

    Each child gets __1 1/2__ pizzas.

2. Find the value of the following.

    (a) $33 \div 6$ 5 R3) 5 3/6

    (b) $25 \div 4$ 6 R1 6 1/4

3. A string is 9 m long. It is cut into 12 equal pieces.
    What is the length of each piece?

    9÷12

    Each piece is _____ m long.   9/12

4. Do these. Show all your working clearly.

(a) Mrs Li bought 21 kg of apples.
She gave the apples equally to 6 friends.
How many kilograms of apples did each friend receive?

(b) Tyrone had $108. He spent $18.
He divided the remaining amount of money equally
among 4 siblings.
How much did each sibling receive?

Exercise 6 : Fraction of a Set

1. Find the value of each of the following.

(a) $\frac{1}{5}$ of 30 =	(b) $\frac{1}{9}$ of 180 =
(c) $\frac{3}{5}$ of 40 =	(d) $\frac{5}{6}$ of 42 =
(e) $\frac{8}{9}$ of 108 =	(f) $\frac{7}{10}$ of 160 =
(g) $20 \times \frac{3}{10}$ =	(h) $20 \times \frac{2}{8}$ =

2. Give each answer in its simplest form.
   (a) Express 40¢ as a fraction of $1.

   (b) Express 60 cm as a fraction of 1 m.

   (c) Express 45 minutes as a fraction of 1 hour.

   (d) What fraction of 1 m is 35 cm?

   (e) What fraction of 1 right angle is 60°?

   (f) What fraction of 1 day is 6 hours?

3. Do these. Show all your work clearly.

   (a) There are 36 peach trees in an orchard. $\frac{2}{9}$ of them are flowering. How many peach trees are not flowering?

   (b) 64 children took part in a singing competition. $\frac{3}{4}$ of them were boys. How many children were girls?

   (c) In a class of 42 students, 14 wear glasses. What fraction of the students wear glasses?

(d) Jane has 60 stamps. 36 of them are Canadian stamps. What fraction of her stamps are Canadian stamps?

(e) Mother bought a bag of 80 buttons. She used 16 of them. What fraction of the buttons were used?

(f) A balsam plant is 25 cm tall. Express 25 cm as a fraction of 1 m.

Unit 4 : Geometry

Right Angles

90°	180°	270°	360°
A $\frac{1}{4}$-turn forms a right angle.	A $\frac{1}{2}$-turn forms two right angles.	A $\frac{3}{4}$-turn forms 3 right angles.	A complete turn forms 4 right angles.

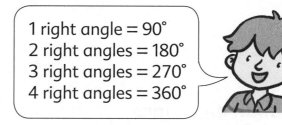

1 right angle = 90°
2 right angles = 180°
3 right angles = 270°
4 right angles = 360°

This angle is less than 90°.

It is called an **acute** angle.

This angle is more than 90°.

It is called an **obtuse** angle.

Acute angle < 90°.
Obtuse angle > 90° but < 180°.

53

Measuring Angles

We use a protractor to measure angles.
We measure angles in degrees.

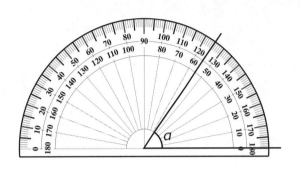

$$\angle a = 55°$$

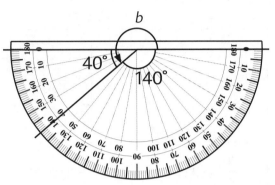

$$\angle b = 180° + 40°$$
$$= 220°$$
$$\text{OR } \angle b = 360° - 140°$$
$$= 220°$$

Perpendicular Lines

Perpendicular lines meet at right angles.

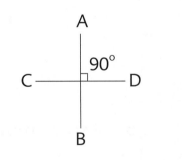

AB and CD are
perpendicular lines.

We say AB is perpendicular to CD.
We write **AB ⊥ CD**.

Primary Mathematics (Standards Edition) Extra Practice 4   © 2008 Marshall Cavendish International (Singapore) Private Limited

Parallel Lines

Parallel lines never meet.

A ———→——— B

C ———→——— D

AB and CD are parallel lines. We draw arrowheads on the lines to show they are parallel.

We say AB is parallel to CD. We write **AB // CD**.

Quadrilaterals

A polygon is a closed figure with straight sides. A **quadrilateral** is a 4-sided polygon.

These are quadrilaterals.

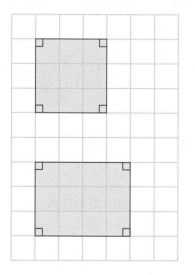

A square has 4 equal sides. It also has 4 equal angles. Each angle = 90°

A rectangle has equal opposite sides. It also has 4 equal angles. Each angle = 90°

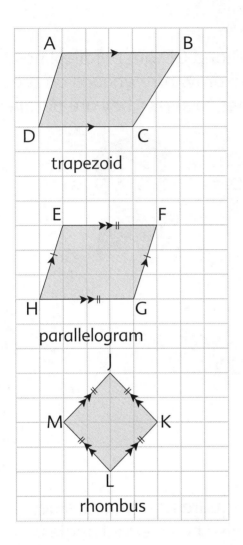

ABCD is a trapezoid.
It has one pair of
parallel lines.

EFGH is a parallelogram.
It has two pairs of
parallel lines which are
equal on opposite sides.

JKLM is a rhombus.
It has two pairs of parallel
lines. It has 4 equal sides.
It is a parallelogram with
equal sides.

We use arrowheads (➤) to show parallel lines.

We use strokes (/) to show equal sides.

Triangles

A **triangle** is a 3-sided polygon.
An equilateral triangle has 3 equal sides.
An isosceles triangle has 2 equal sides.
A scalene triangle has no equal sides.
An equilateral triangle is also an isosceles triangle.

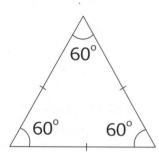

equilateral triangle

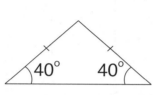

isosceles triangle

scalene triangle

Circles

A **circle** is a closed figure. It is not a polygon because it does not have straight sides.
The diameters of a circle pass through its centre.
The diameters are equal.
The radius of a circle is measured from its centre to its edge.
The radius is $\frac{1}{2}$ the length of the diameter.

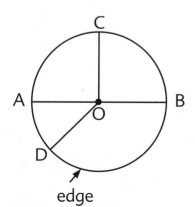

edge

O is the centre of the circle.
AB is a diameter.
OC is a radius.
OD is also a radius.
AB = 2 × OC

57

Solid Figures

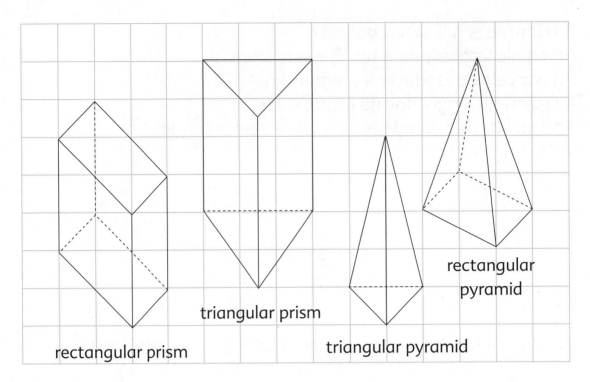

triangular prism

rectangular pyramid

rectangular prism

triangular pyramid

A **rectangular prism** has 6 faces.
Each face is a rectangle.

A **triangular prism** has 5 faces.
3 of its faces are rectangles.
2 of its faces are triangles.

A **triangular pyramid** has 4 faces.
Each face is a triangle.

A **rectangular pyramid** has 5 faces.
4 of its faces are triangles.
1 of its faces is a rectangle.

A **solid cylinder** has a curved surface.
It has 2 flat faces.

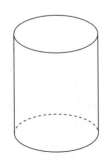

cylinder

Nets

A **net** of a solid is a figure which folds to form the solid.

A cube has more than one net.

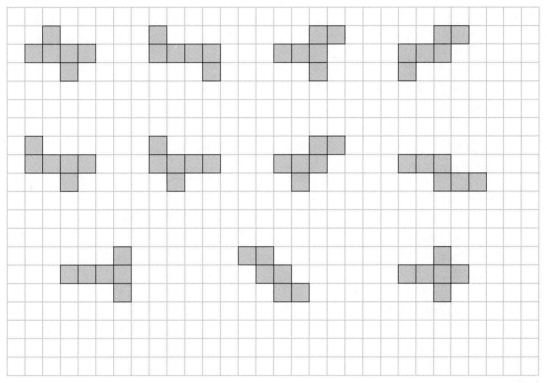

Nets of a cube

Primary Mathematics (Standards Edition) Extra Practice 4

Blank

Exercise 1 : Right Angles

1. Mark all the right angles in each figure. Then complete the sentence below it.

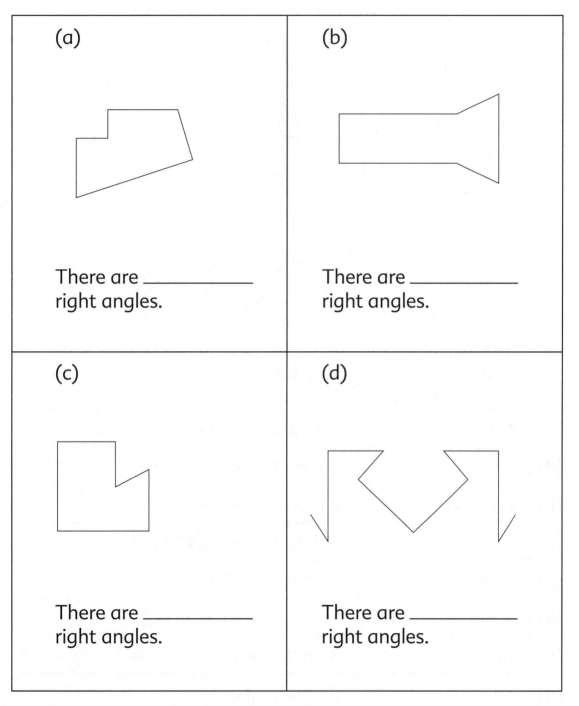

(a)

There are _____ right angles.

(b)

There are _____ right angles.

(c)

There are _____ right angles.

(d)

There are _____ right angles.

Primary Mathematics (Standards Edition) Extra Practice 4

2. Use the picture to help you complete the table below.

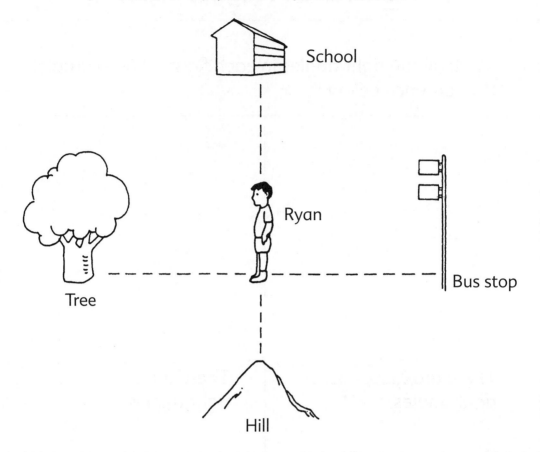

School

Ryan

Tree

Bus stop

Hill

	Ryan is facing the	If he turns	He will face the
E.g.	tree	1 right angle to the right	school
(a)	tree	3 right angles to the left	
(b)	bus stop	2 right angles	
(c)	bus stop	3 right angles to the left	
(d)	school	4 right angles	
(e)	school	1 right angle to the right	
(f)	hill	3 right angles to the left	
(g)	hill	2 right angles	

Exercise 2 : Measuring Angles

1. List all the marked angles in the table below.

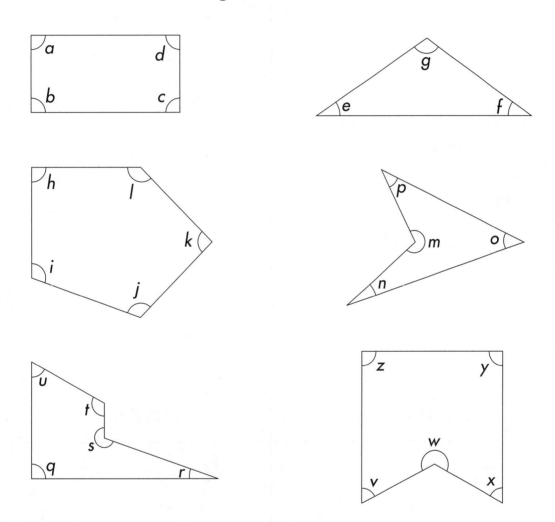

(a)	Right angles	
(b)	Smaller than a right angle	
(c)	Greater than a right angle	

2. Measure the marked angles.

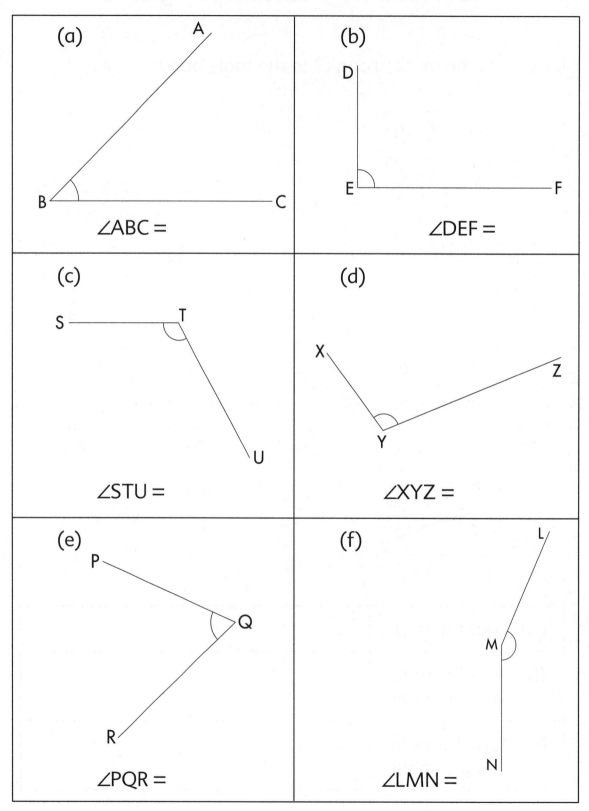

(a)

∠ABC =

(b)

∠DEF =

(c)

∠STU =

(d)

∠XYZ =

(e)

∠PQR =

(f)

∠LMN =

Primary Mathematics (Standards Edition) Extra Practice 4

© 2008 Marshall Cavendish International (Singapore) Private Limited

3. Use the marked end point of each line to make the required angle. Mark the angle.

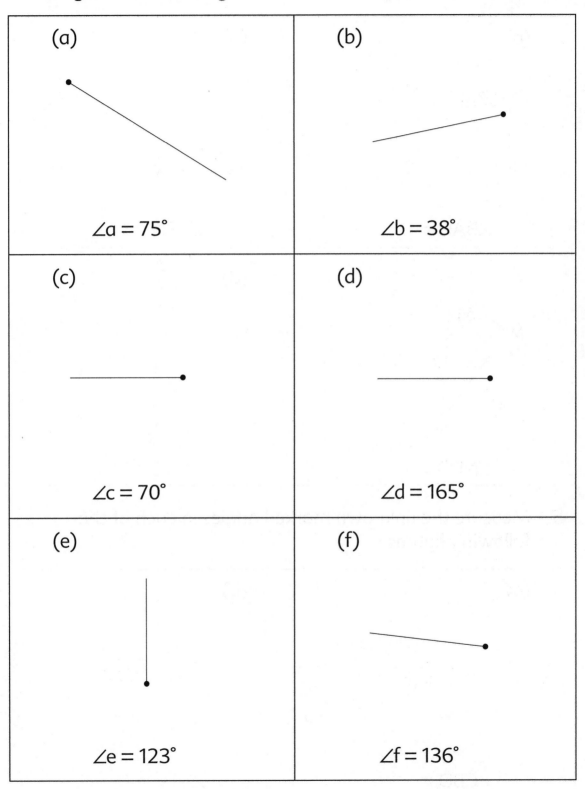

(a)

$\angle a = 75°$

(b)

$\angle b = 38°$

(c)

$\angle c = 70°$

(d)

$\angle d = 165°$

(e)

$\angle e = 123°$

(f)

$\angle f = 136°$

4. Measure the unknown marked angles in each of the following rectangles.

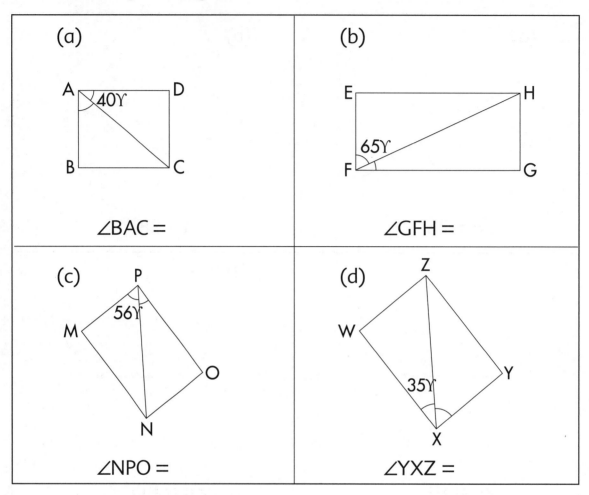

(a)

∠BAC =

(b)

∠GFH =

(c)

∠NPO =

(d)

∠YXZ =

5. Measure the unknown marked angles in each of the following figures.

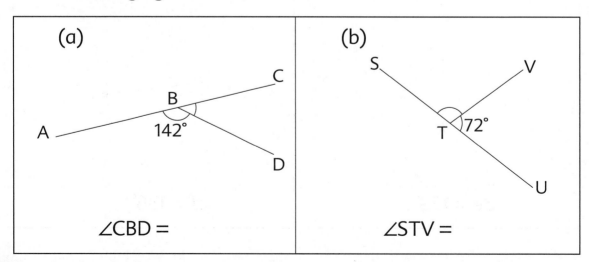

(a)

∠CBD =

(b)

∠STV =

Primary Mathematics (Standards Edition) Extra Practice 4

© 2008 Marshall Cavendish International (Singapore) Private Limited

6. Fill in the blanks.

  (a) A complete turn is _____ right angles.

    It is _____ degrees.

  (b) $\frac{1}{2}$ of a complete turn is _____ right angles.

    It is _____ degrees.

  (c) $\frac{1}{4}$ of a complete turn is _____ right angle.

    It is _____ degrees.

  (d) $\frac{3}{4}$ of a complete turn is _____ right angles.

    It is _____ degrees.

7. Measure the marked angles.

  (a)   (b)

  $\angle a =$ _____ $\angle b =$ _____

Primary Mathematics (Standards Edition) Extra Practice 4

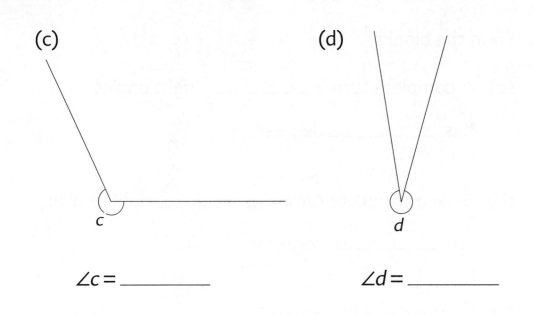

(c)

∠c = _____

(d)

∠d = _____

Exercise 3 : Perpendicular Lines

1. Name each pair of perpendicular lines.

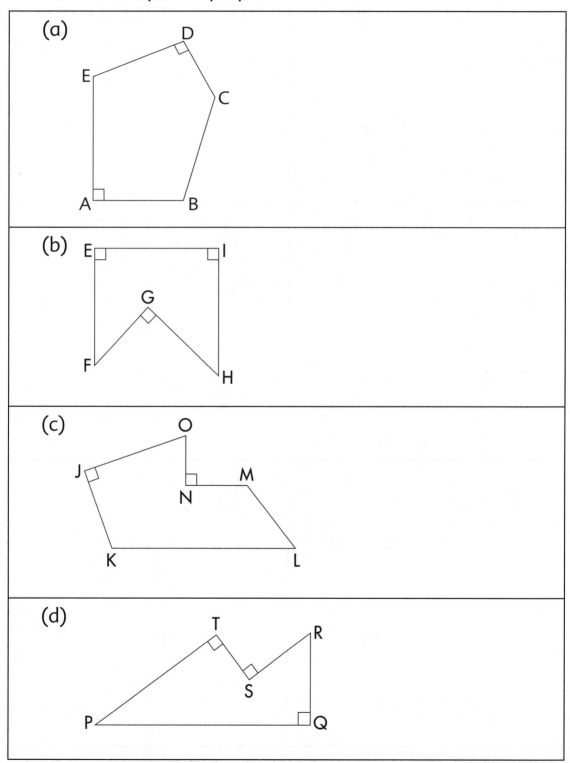

(a)

(b)

(c)

(d)

2. Draw a line perpendicular to each of the given lines through the point P.

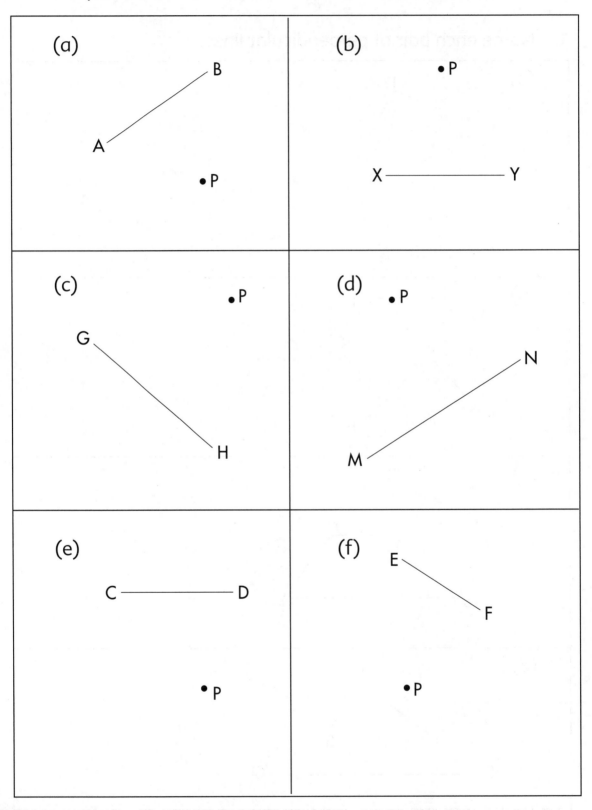

Exercise 4 : Parallel Lines

1. Name all the pairs of parallel lines.

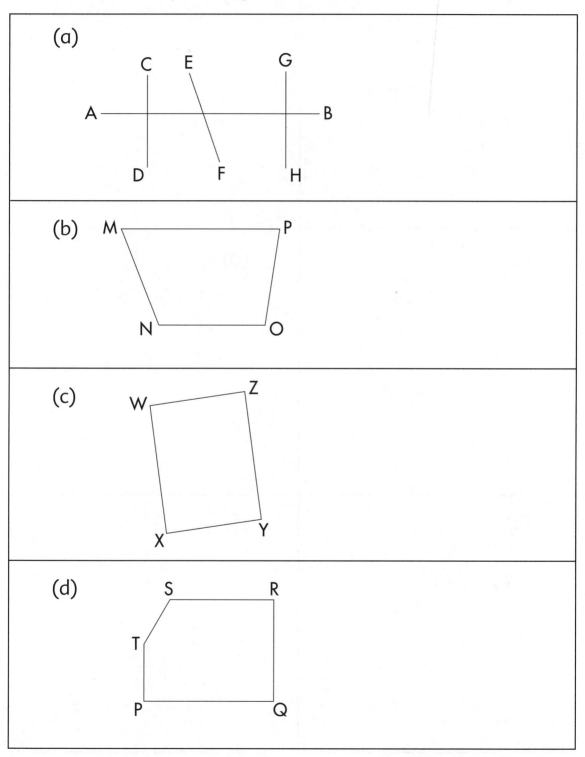

(a)

(b)

(c)

(d)

2. Use a set-square and a ruler to draw a line parallel to each of the given lines through the point P.

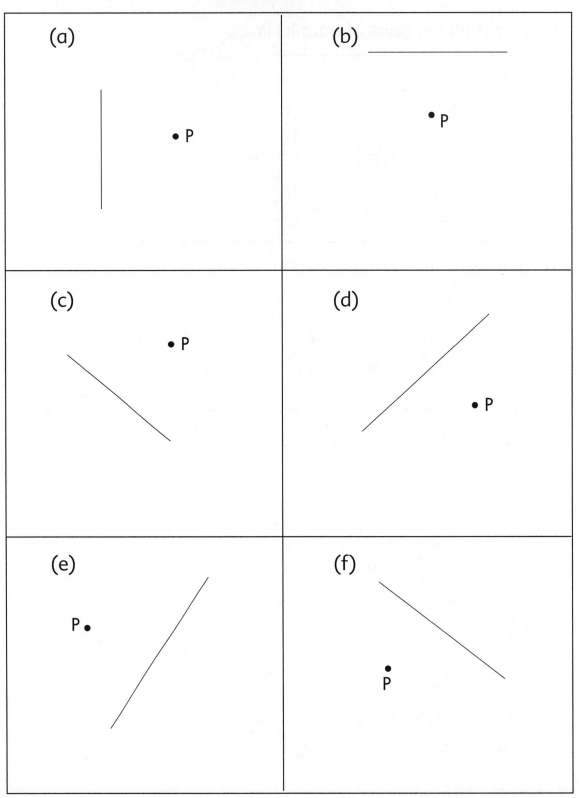

(a)

• P

(b) _____

• P

(c)

• P

(d)

• P

(e)

P •

(f)

•
P

Primary Mathematics (Standards Edition) Extra Practice 4

Exercise 5 : Quadrilaterals

1. Name the following figures.

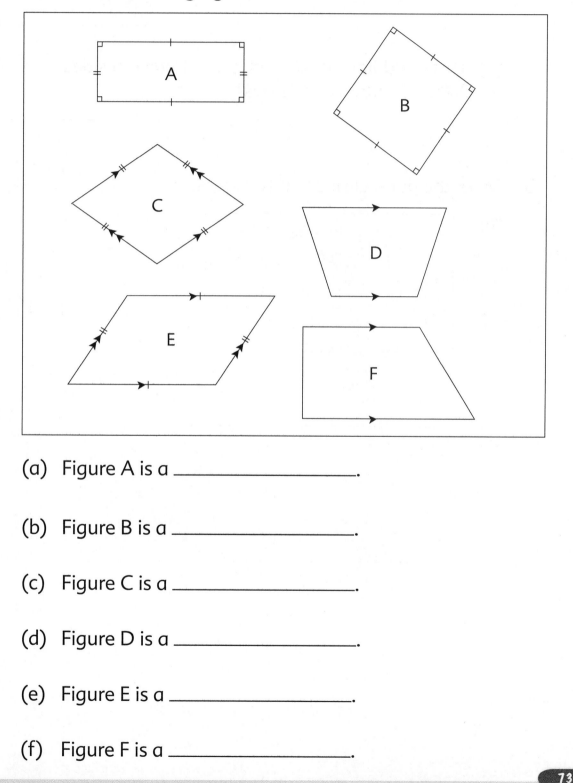

(a) Figure A is a _____.

(b) Figure B is a _____.

(c) Figure C is a _____.

(d) Figure D is a _____.

(e) Figure E is a _____.

(f) Figure F is a _____.

2. Identify the quadrilateral in each case.

   (a) This quadrilateral has 2 pairs of parallel lines.
       None of the angles is 90°. What quadrilateral is this?

       _____

   (b) This quadrilateral has one pair of parallel sides.
       What quadrilateral is this?

       _____

3. Mark the parallel sides in the figure.

   (a)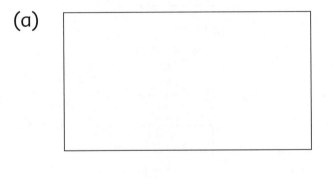

   (b)

Exercise 6 : Triangles

1. Which of the following are **right**, **isosceles** or **equilateral** triangles? Name them.

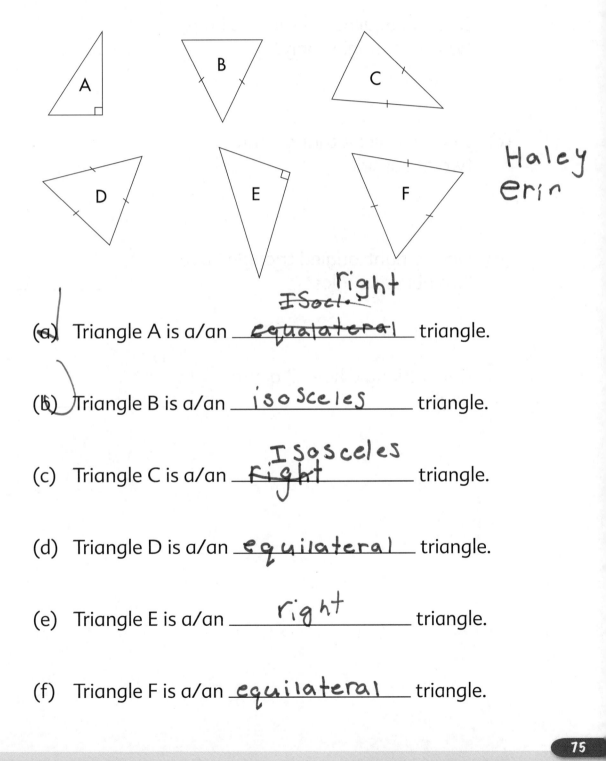

Haley
erin

(a) Triangle A is a/an ~~equalateral~~ ~~ISoct.~~ **right** triangle.

(b) Triangle B is a/an __isosceles__ triangle.

(c) Triangle C is a/an ~~right~~ **Isosceles** triangle.

(d) Triangle D is a/an __equilateral__ triangle.

(e) Triangle E is a/an __right__ triangle.

(f) Triangle F is a/an __equilateral__ triangle.

Primary Mathematics (Standards Edition) Extra Practice 4

2. Write 'Yes' or 'No' in each blank.

(a) Does a triangle have 3 vertices? _____

(b) Does an equilateral triangle have
     two equal angles only? _____

(c) Does a scalene triangle have
     two equal sides? _____

(d) Does a right-angled triangle have
     two obtuse angles? _____

(e) Can a triangle have 3 acute
     angles? _____

Primary Mathematics (Standards Edition) Extra Practice 4

Exercise 7 : Circles

1. Look at the circle. Then name the parts correctly.

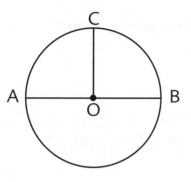

   In the circle above,

   (a) O is the _____,

   (b) AB is the _____,

   (c) OC is the _____.

2. Fill in the blanks.

   (a) The diameter of a circle is 10 cm.

      Its radius is _____ cm.

   (b) The radius of a circle is 18 cm.

      Its diameter is _____ cm.

Primary Mathematics (Standards Edition) Extra Practice 4

3. Write 'Yes' or 'No' in each blank.

   (a) Does a circle have no corners?   _____

   (b) Does a circle have vertices?   _____

   (c) Is the length of the diameter of a circle
        half the length of its radius?   _____

   (d) Does the diameter of a circle pass
        through its centre?   _____

   (e) Is the length of the radius of a circle
        half the length of its diameter?   _____

Primary Mathematics (Standards Edition) Extra Practice 4

Exercise 8 : Solid Figures

1. Identify the solid figure shown in each case.

   (a)

   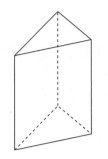

   _____

   (b)

   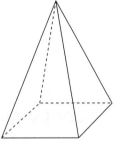

   _____

   (c)

   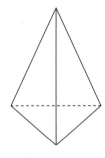

   _____

   (d)

   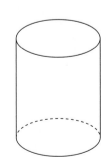

   _____

2. Fill in the blanks.

(a) How many faces of a rectangular pyramid are triangles?

_____

(b) How many faces of a rectangular prism are rectangles?

_____

(c) How many faces of a cylinder are squares?

_____

(d) How many faces of a triangular pyramid are triangles?

_____

Exercise 9 : Nets

1. The figures show the nets of some solids.

   (a)

   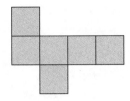

   What is this solid figure? _____

   (b)

   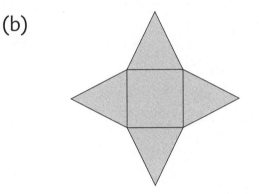

   What is this solid figure? _____

   (c)

   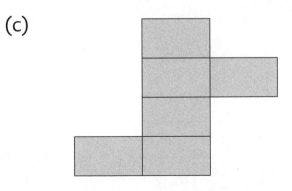

   What is this solid figure? _____

2. Draw the shape of the net of each solid.

(a)

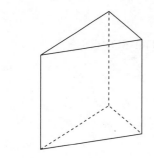

(b)

(c)

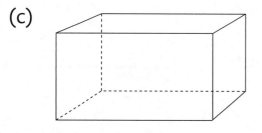

Unit 5 : Area and Perimeter

Friendly Notes

Area of a Rectangle

Area of a rectangle = length × width

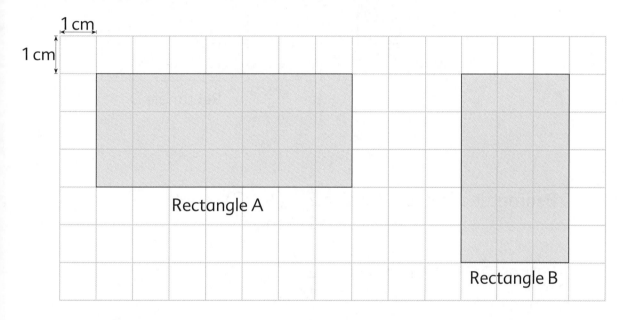

Rectangle A

Rectangle B

Each square in the grid has an area of 1 cm².
Rectangle A has an area of 21 cm².
Rectangle B has an area of 15 cm².

Other units of area:
Square inch (in²)
Square meter (m²)
Square kilometer (km²)
Square foot (ft²)
Square yard (yd²)
Square mile (mi²)

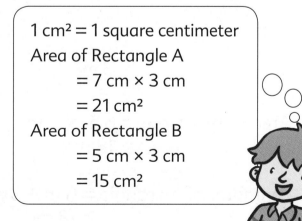

1 cm² = 1 square centimeter
Area of Rectangle A
= 7 cm × 3 cm
= 21 cm²
Area of Rectangle B
= 5 cm × 3 cm
= 15 cm²

Perimeter of a Rectangle

Perimeter of a rectangle = 2 × (length + width)

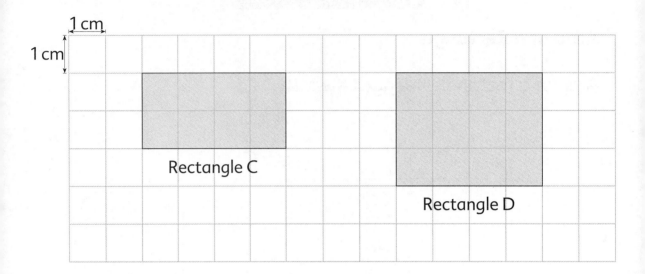

Perimeter of Rectangle C = 2 × (4 + 2)
                                          = 12 cm

Perimeter of Rectangle D = 2 × (4 + 3)
                                          = 14 cm

1. Find the area and perimeter of the rectangle below.

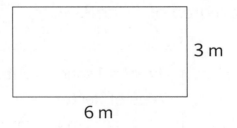

Area of rectangle = 6 m × 3 m
                              = 18 m²

Perimeter of rectangle = 6 m + 3 m + 6 m + 3 m
                                    = 18 m

Composite Figures

A **composite figure** is made up of more than one shape.

Find the area and perimeter of the figure below.

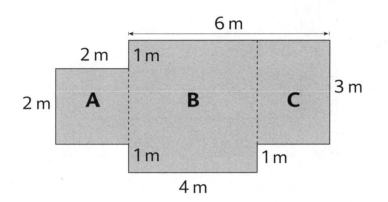

Area of figure = Area of A + Area of B + Area of C
$$= (2 \times 2)\text{ m}^2 + (4 \times 4)\text{ m}^2 + (3 \times 2)\text{ m}^2$$
$$= 4\text{ m}^2 + 16\text{ m}^2 + 6\text{ m}^2$$
$$= 26\text{ m}^2$$

Perimeter of figure = $(6 + 3 + 2 + 1 + 4 + 1 + 2 + 2 + 2 + 1)$ m
$$= 24\text{ m}$$

Primary Mathematics (Standards Edition) Extra Practice 4

2. Find the area of the shaded part of the figure.

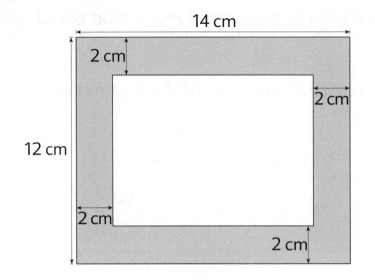

Area of big rectangle = 14 cm × 12 cm
                     = 168 cm²

Area of small rectangle = 10 cm × 8 cm
                       = 80 cm²

14 − 4 = 10
12 − 4 = 8
Length of small rectangle is 10 cm.
Width of small rectangle is 8 cm.

Exercise 1 : Area of Rectangles

1. Find the area and perimeter of each rectangle or square.

(a)

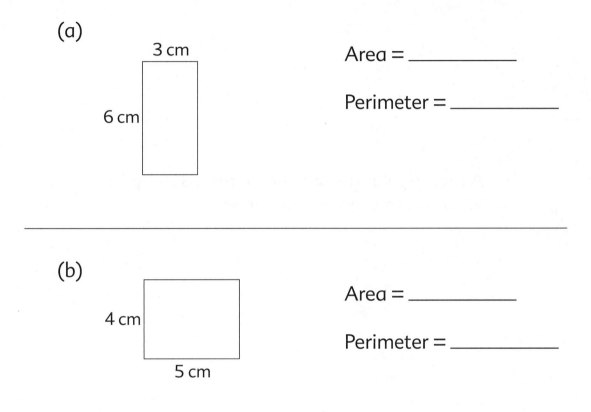

3 cm

6 cm

Area = _____

Perimeter = _____

(b)

4 cm

5 cm

Area = _____

Perimeter = _____

2. Find the unknown side and the area of the rectangle.

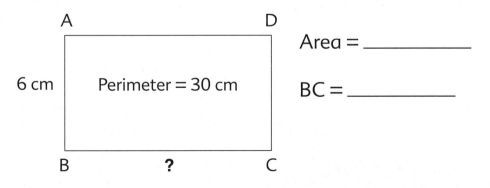

A   D

6 cm

Perimeter = 30 cm

B   ?   C

Area = _____

BC = _____

Primary Mathematics (Standards Edition) Extra Practice 4

3. Do these. Show all your work clearly.

(a) Kyle uses 18 old stamps to make a picture. She lays them side by side. If each stamp measures 3 cm by 2 cm, find the area of the picture.

(b) A rectangular garden measures 28 m by 16 m. What is the area of the garden?

(c) Cameron wants to carpet his living room floor, which measures 8 yd by 4 yd. If the carpet costs $15 per square yard, how much must Cameron pay to buy the carpet he needs?

Exercise 2 : Perimeter of Rectangles

1. Find the unknown side and the perimeter of each of the following rectangles.

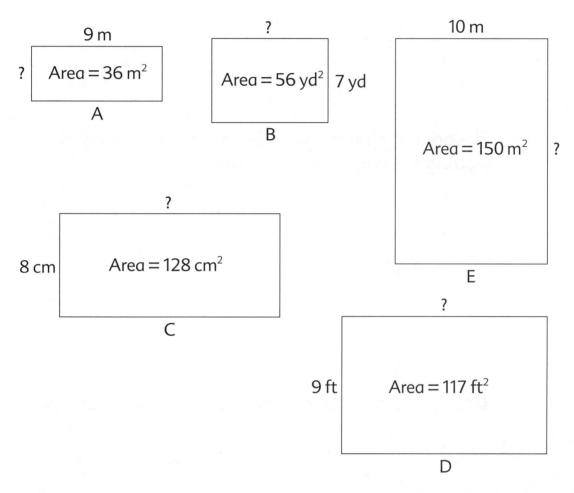

	Figure	Area	Length	Width	Perimeter
(a)	A	36 m²	9 m		
(b)	B	56 yd²		7 yd	
(c)	C	128 cm²		8 cm	
(d)	D	117 ft²		9 ft	
(e)	E	150 m²		10 m	

2. Do these. Show all your work clearly.

   (a) The area of a rectangle is 30 m². If the length of the rectangle is 6 m, find its width and perimeter.

   (b) The area of a rectangle is 24 in.². If the width of the rectangle is 4 in., find its perimeter.

   (c) The square and the rectangle have the same perimeter.

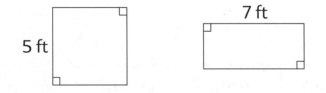

   (i) Find the width of the rectangle.

   (ii) Which figure has a bigger area?

Exercise 3 : Composite Figures

1. Find the perimeter of each of the following figures.
   (All lines meet at right angles.)

   (a)

   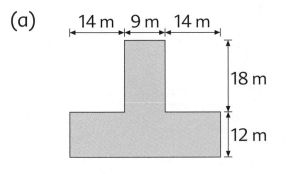

   (b)

   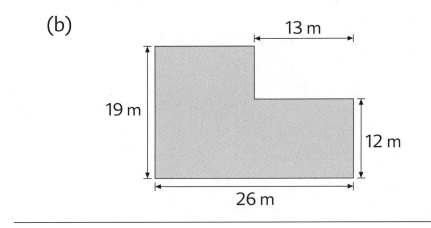

   (c)

   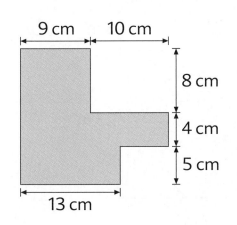

2. Find the area of each of the following figures.
   (All lines meet at right angles.)

(a)

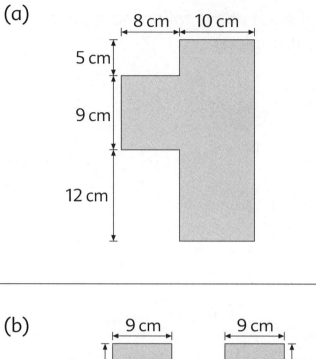

(b)

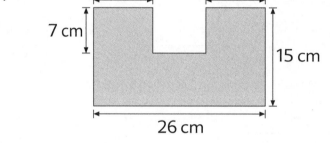

(c)

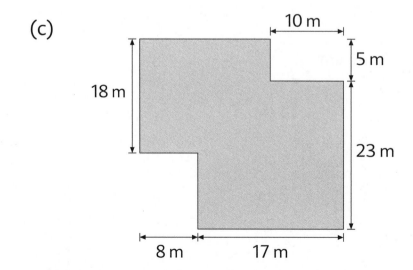

3. Find the area of the shaded part of each rectangle.

(a)

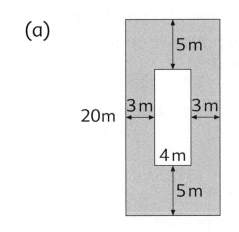

(b)

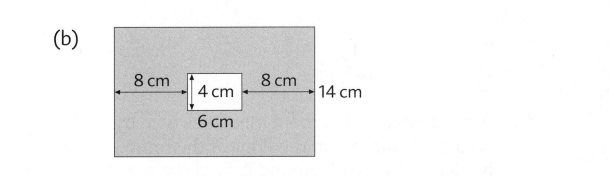

(c)

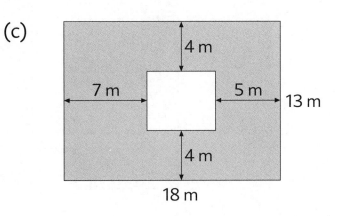

4. Do these. Show all your work clearly.

   (a) A rectangular garden measures 28 ft by 15 ft.
       A concrete path 1 ft wide is paved around it.
       What is the area of the path?

       28 ft

       15 ft

   (b) A rectangular living room measures 6 yd by 5 yd.
       A carpet is placed on the floor of the room leaving a
       border 1 yd wide all around it. Find the area of the
       border.

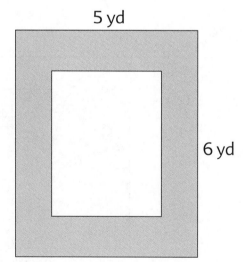

       5 yd

       6 yd

Primary Mathematics (Standards Edition) Extra Practice 4   © 2008 Marshall Cavendish International (Singapore) Private Limited

Unit 6 : Decimals

Tenths

When we divide one whole into 10 equal parts, each part is $\frac{1}{10}$ or **0.1**.

0.1 is a **decimal**. It stands for **1 tenth**.

The dot in a decimal is called a **decimal point**. The decimal point separates the whole from the fractional part.

1. Write $\frac{4}{10}$ as a decimal.

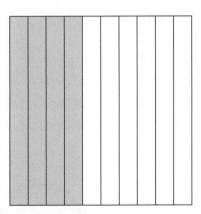

0.4 is read as 'zero point four' or 'four tenths'.

$$\frac{4}{10} = 0.4$$

2. Write $2\frac{3}{10}$ as a decimal.

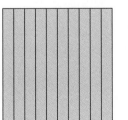 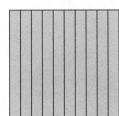

$$2\frac{3}{10} = 2.3$$

Primary Mathematics (Standards Edition) Extra Practice 4

Hundredths

When we divide one whole into 100 equal parts, each part is $\frac{1}{100}$ or **0.01**.

0.01 stands for **1 hundredth**.
0.01 has two decimal places.

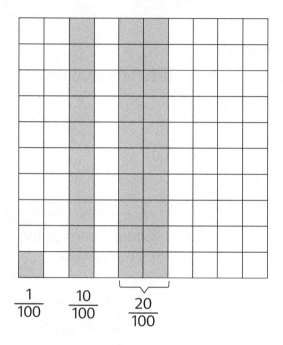

$$\frac{1}{100} = 0.01$$

$$\frac{10}{100} = 0.10$$

$$\frac{20}{100} = 0.20$$

$\frac{1}{100}$ $\frac{10}{100}$ $\frac{20}{100}$

We read 0.01 as 'zero point zero one' or 'one hundredth'.
We read 0.10 as 'zero point one zero' or 'one tenth' and 0.20 as 'zero point two zero' or 'two tenths'.

1. Write $2\frac{31}{100}$ as a decimal.

$$2\frac{31}{100} = 2.31$$

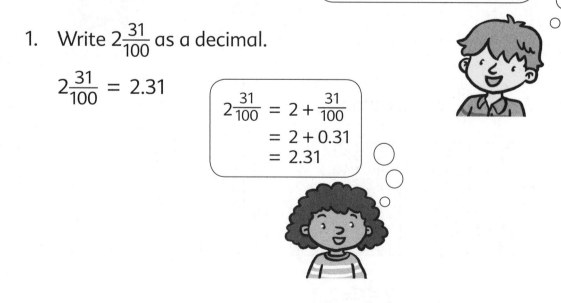

$$2\frac{31}{100} = 2 + \frac{31}{100}$$
$$= 2 + 0.31$$
$$= 2.31$$

Thousandths

When we divide a whole into 1000 equal parts, each part is $\frac{1}{1000}$ or **0.001**.

0.001 stands for **one thousandth**.

0.001 has three decimal places.

1. Write a decimal for each of the following.

   (a) 5 ones 3 thousandths = 5.003

   (b) 8 tens 6 ones 5 tenths 2 thousandths
        = 86.502

   (c) 4 tens 8 tenths 2 hundredths 9 thousandths
        = 40.829

We read 40.829 as 'forty point eight two nine' or 'forty and eight hundred twenty-nine thousandths'.

Rounding

We can use a number line, place value chart or follow rules in rounding to help us round numbers.

Rules in Rounding

Look at the digit in the preceding place value. If the digit is 1, 2, 3 or 4, we round down. If the digit is 5, 6, 7, 8 or 9, we round up.

Round number to the nearest	Look at the digit in the	Digit is 1 to 4	Digit is 5 to 9
whole number	tenths place	Round down	Round up
ten	ones place		
tenth	hundredths place		
hundredth	thousandths place		

1. Round 27.543 to the nearest

    (a) whole number,   (b) ten,

    (c) tenth,   (d) hundredth.

Place Value Chart

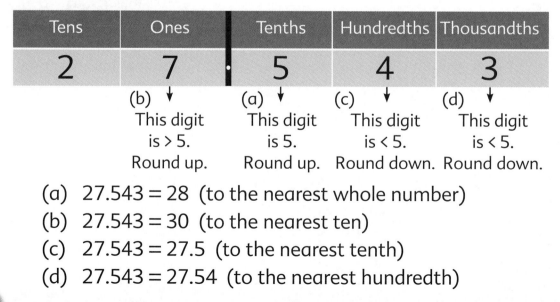

Tens	Ones	Tenths	Hundredths	Thousandths
2	7	5	4	3

    (b)   (a)   (c)   (d)

This digit is > 5. Round up.   This digit is 5. Round up.   This digit is < 5. Round down.   This digit is < 5. Round down.

(a) $27.543 = 28$ (to the nearest whole number)

(b) $27.543 = 30$ (to the nearest ten)

(c) $27.543 = 27.5$ (to the nearest tenth)

(d) $27.543 = 27.54$ (to the nearest hundredth)

Exercise 1 : Tenths

1. Write each fraction as a decimal.

(a) $\dfrac{3}{10}$ = 0.3	(b) $\dfrac{8}{10}$ = 0.8
(c) $3\dfrac{5}{10}$ = 3.5	(d) $1\dfrac{6}{10}$ = 1.6
(e) $2\dfrac{7}{10}$ = 2.7	(f) $4\dfrac{9}{10}$ = 4.9

2. Write each decimal as a fraction in its simplest form.

(a) 0.6 = $\dfrac{6}{10}$ = $\dfrac{3}{5}$	(b) 1.8 = $\dfrac{18}{10}$ = $1\dfrac{4}{5}$
(c) 3.4 =	(d) 5.3 = $5\dfrac{3}{10}$

3. Fill in the blanks.

   (a) 0.9 = _____9_____ tenths   (b) 1.3 = _____13_____ tenths

   (c) 2.5 = _____25_____ tenths   (d) 8.6 = _____86_____ tenths

4. Write the numbers in decimals.

   (a) 6 ones 5 tenths = _____6.5_____

   (b) 3 ones 9 tenths = _____3.9_____

   (c) 5 tens 2 ones 6 tenths = _____52.6_____

   (d) 8 tens 8 tenths = _____80.8_____

5. Fill in the missing decimal or whole number in each box.

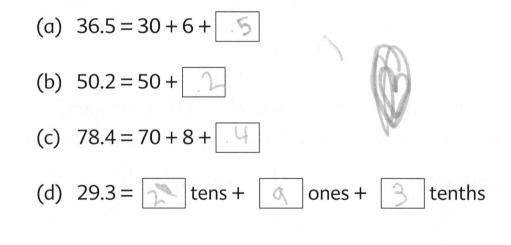

   (a) $36.5 = 30 + 6 + \boxed{.5}$

   (b) $50.2 = 50 + \boxed{.2}$

   (c) $78.4 = 70 + 8 + \boxed{.4}$

   (d) $29.3 = \boxed{2}$ tens + $\boxed{9}$ ones + $\boxed{3}$ tenths

6. Complete the following regular number patterns.

   (a) 0.7, 0.8, $\boxed{0.9}$, $\boxed{1.0}$, 1.1, 1.2

   (b) 0.5, 1, $\boxed{1.5}$, $\boxed{2.0}$, 2.5, 3

Primary Mathematics (Standards Edition) Extra Practice 4   © 2008 Marshall Cavendish International (Singapore) Private Limited

Exercise 2 : Hundredths

1. Write each fraction as a decimal.

(a) $\frac{5}{100} = 0.05$	(b) $\frac{8}{100} = 0.08$
(c) $\frac{39}{100} = 0.39$	(d) $\frac{63}{100} = 0.63$
(e) $10\frac{99}{100} = 10.99$	(f) $9\frac{56}{100} = 9.56$

2. Fill in the blanks.

   (a) In 28.09, the digit 9 is in the ____hundredths____ place.

   Its value is ____$\frac{9}{100}$____.

   (b) In 80.65, the digit 6 is in the ____tenths____ place.

   Its value is ____$\frac{6}{10}$____.

3. Write the value of each of the following as a decimal.

   (a) $29 + \frac{3}{100} = 29.03$ (b) $62 + \frac{5}{10} + \frac{1}{100} =$

4. Fill in the missing decimals.

(a) $8.88 = 8 + 0.8 +$ $\boxed{.06}$

(b) $12.07 = 10 + 2 +$ $\boxed{.7}$

(c) $34.45 = 30 + 4 +$ $\boxed{.4}$ $+ 0.05$

(d) $59.11 = 50 + 9 +$ $\boxed{.1}$ $+$ $\boxed{.01}$

5. Fill in the blanks.

(a) $0.05 =$ _____ 5 _____ hundredths

(b) $0.36 =$ _____ 36 _____ hundredths

(c) $0.7 =$ _____ 7 _____ hundredths

(d) $1 =$ _____ 1 _____ hundredths

(e) $1.8 =$ _____ 18 _____ hundredths

6. Complete the following regular number patterns.

(a) $0.25,$ $0.2,$ $\boxed{1.5}$ $,$ $\boxed{1}$ $,$ 0.05

(b) $2,$ $1.75,$ $1.5,$ $\boxed{0.25}$ $\boxed{0.50}$ 0.75

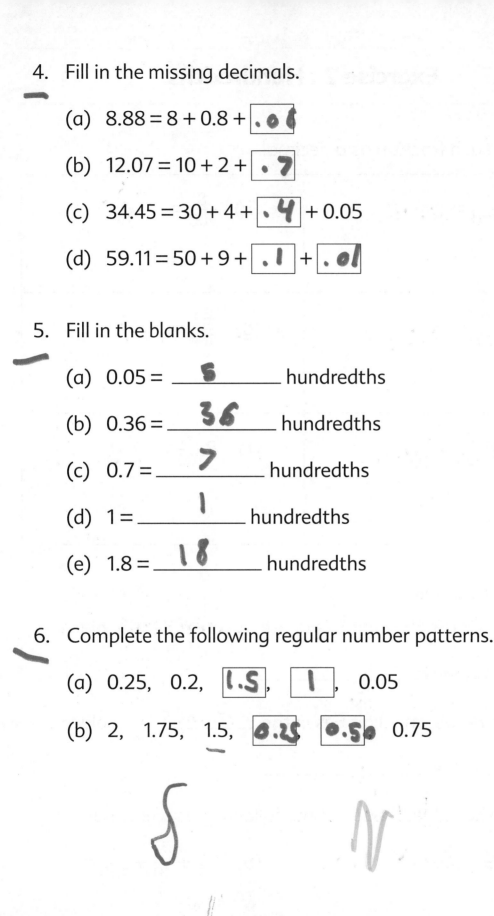

Primary Mathematics (Standards Edition) Extra Practice 4

7. Write each decimal as a fraction in its simplest form.

(a) $0.25 =$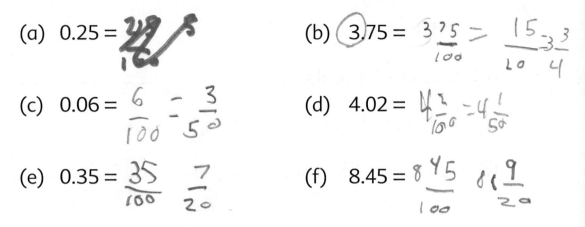

(b) $3.75 = 3\frac{75}{100} = \frac{15}{20}3\frac{3}{4}$

(c) $0.06 = \frac{6}{100} = \frac{3}{50}$

(d) $4.02 = 4\frac{2}{100} = 4\frac{1}{50}$

(e) $0.35 = \frac{35}{100}\ \frac{7}{20}$

(f) $8.45 = 8\frac{45}{100}\ 8\frac{9}{20}$

8. Change the denominator to 10 or 100. Then write the fraction as a decimal.

(a) $\frac{1}{5} = \frac{2}{10}$

0.2

(b) $5\frac{1}{2} = 5\frac{5}{10}\ 5.50$

(c) $10\frac{2}{5} = \frac{4}{10}$

10.40

(d) $\frac{1}{4} = \frac{25}{100}\ 0.25$

25.00

(e) $\frac{3}{4} = \frac{75}{100}\ 0.75$

(f) $2\frac{3}{4} = 2\frac{75}{100}$

2.75

(g) $\frac{19}{20} = \frac{95}{100}$

0.95

(h) $4\frac{12}{25} = \frac{100}{100}$

$\frac{48}{100}$

4.48

9. Write each amount of money as a decimal.

   (a) 2 dollars 17 cents   _____2.17_____

   (b) 5 dollars 25 cents   _____5.25_____

   (c) 10 dollars 80 cents   _____10.80_____

   (d) 195 dollars 65 cents   _____195.65_____

10. Circle the greatest value.

   (a) 20.07, (20.70,) 20.17

   (b) 368.18, 368.80, (368.81)

   (c) 1042.46, 104.46, (1042.64)

   (d) 21,672.99, 21,672.89, (21,762.98)

Exercise 3 : Thousandths

1. Write each fraction as a decimal.

   (a) $\dfrac{7}{1000} =$ **0.007**

   (b) $\dfrac{15}{1000} =$ 0.015

   (c) $\dfrac{23}{1000} =$

   (d) $\dfrac{107}{1000} =$

   (e) $\dfrac{135}{1000} =$

   (f) $2\dfrac{3}{1000} =$

   (g) $9\dfrac{5}{1000} =$

   (h) $30\dfrac{18}{1000} =$

2. Fill in the blanks.

   (a) In 7.328, the digit 8 is in the _____ place.

   Its value is _____.

   (b) In 59.043, the digit 3 is in the _____ place.

   Its value is _____.

3. Fill in the missing decimals.

   (a) $6.512 = 6 + 0.5 + 0.01 +$ ☐

   (b) $23.086 = 23 + 0.08 +$ ☐

   (c) $10.227 = 10 + 0.2 + 0.02 +$ ☐

4. Fill in the blanks.

   (a) $0.007 =$ ___7___ thousandths

   (b) $0.039 =$ ___39___ thousandths

   (c) $1 =$ ___4000___ thousandths

5. Write the value of each of the following as a decimal.

   (a) $12 + \dfrac{1}{1000} =$ ___12.001___

   (b) $8 + \dfrac{25}{1000} =$ ___8.025___

   (c) $25 + \dfrac{4}{10} + \dfrac{3}{1000} =$ ___25.403___

   (d) $7 + \dfrac{6}{100} + \dfrac{8}{1000} =$ ___7.068___

   (e) 2 thousandths = ___0.002___

   (f) 3 hundredths 8 thousandths = ___0.038___

   (g) 7 tenths 5 thousandths = ___0.705___

   (h) 6 ones 6 thousandths = ___6.006___

   (i) 9 tens 9 thousandths = ___90.009___

   (j) 2 hundreds 3 tenths 5 thousandths

       = ___2000.305___

6. Circle the smallest number in each set.

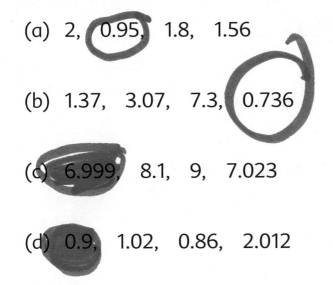

(a) 2, (0.95), 1.8, 1.56

(b) 1.37, 3.07, 7.3, (0.736)

(c) (6.999), 8.1, 9, 7.023

(d) (0.9), 1.02, 0.86, 2.012

7. Circle the greatest number in each set.

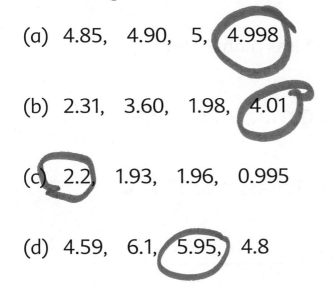

(a) 4.85, 4.90, 5, (4.998)

(b) 2.31, 3.60, 1.98, (4.01)

(c) (2.2), 1.93, 1.96, 0.995

(d) 4.59, 6.1, (5.95), 4.8

8. Fill in the blanks.

(a) 0.1 more than 29.9 is _____.

(b) _____ is 0.01 less than 59.69.

(c) _____ is 0.01 more than 83.9.

(d) 0.001 more than 62.29 is _____.

(e) 0.1 more than 76.89 is _____.

(f) _____ is 0.1 less than 28.93.

(g) _____ is 0.001 more than 19.99.

(h) _____ is 0.001 less than 30.1.

(i) 0.001 less than 1 is _____.

(j) 0.01 more than 5.99 is _____.

Primary Mathematics (Standards Edition) Extra Practice 4

Exercise 4 : Rounding

1. Fill in the blanks.

   (a) 5.6 is _____ when rounded to the nearest whole number.

   (b) 12.3 is _____ when rounded to the nearest whole number.

   (c) 29.43 is _____ when rounded to the nearest whole number.

   (d) 60.51 is _____ when rounded to the nearest whole number.

2. Round each of the following to the nearest tenth.

   (a) 58.92 _____   (b) 34.36 _____

   (c) 399.63 _____   (d) 205.05 _____

   (e) $15.25 _____   (f) $65.73 _____

3. Round each of the following to the nearest hundredth.

   (a) 69.052 _____   (b) 86.535 _____

   (c) 35.688 _____   (d) 164.569 _____

   (e) 561.955 _____   (f) 216.243 _____

4. Round each of the following to the nearest kilogram.

   (a) 36.54 kg _____   (b) 59.4 kg _____

5. Round each of the following to the nearest yard.

   (a) 22.15 yd _____   (b) 91.52 yd _____

6. Round each of the following to the nearest liter.

   (a) 4.63 ℓ _____   (b) 17.45 ℓ _____

7. Round each of the following to the nearest kilometer.

   (a) 64.48 km _____   (b) 529.7 km _____

8. Choose the best answer and write it in the box.

   Diana weighs about 35 kg. Which one of the following could be her actual weight?

   34.45 kg,   35.60 kg,   34.35 kg,   35.38 kg

   _____

Primary Mathematics (Standards Edition) Extra Practice 4   © 2008 Marshall Cavendish International (Singapore) Private Limited

Unit 7 : The Four Operations of Decimals

Addition and Subtraction

We add and subtract decimals in the same way as whole numbers. We have to put the decimal point correctly.

1. Find the value of

   (a) 2.9 + 3.6

   $$
   \begin{array}{r}
   \overset{1}{2}.9 \\
   +\ \ 3.6 \\
   \hline
   6.5
   \end{array}
   $$

   (b) 3.65 − 0.32

   $$
   \begin{array}{r}
   3.65 \\
   -\ \ 0.32 \\
   \hline
   3.33
   \end{array}
   $$

2. Estimate each value. Then add.

   $$
   \begin{aligned}
   12.61 + 8.9 &\approx 13 + 9 \\
   &= 22
   \end{aligned}
   $$
   The answer is reasonable.

   $$
   \begin{array}{r}
   \overset{1}{1}\overset{1}{2}.61 \\
   +\ \ \ \ 8.9 \\
   \hline
   21.51
   \end{array}
   $$

3. Estimate the value. Then subtract.

   $$
   \begin{aligned}
   15.94 - 6.03 &\approx 16 - 6 \\
   &= 10
   \end{aligned}
   $$
   The answer is reasonable.

   $$
   \begin{array}{r}
   15.94 \\
   -\ \ 6.03 \\
   \hline
   9.91
   \end{array}
   $$

Primary Mathematics (Standards Edition) Extra Practice 4

Multiplication

We multiply decimals in the same way as whole numbers.
Then we put the decimal point according to the total number
of decimal places in the decimals that are multiplied.

1. Multiply 6.14 by 5.

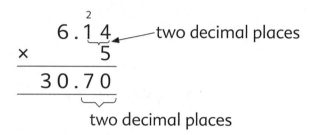

$$
\begin{array}{r}
{}^{2} \\
6.14 \\
\times5 \\
\hline
30.70 \\
\hline
\end{array}
$$

two decimal places

two decimal places

2. Estimate the product of 35.02 and 7.

$$
\begin{array}{r}
{}^{3} \\
35 \\
\times7 \\
\hline
245 \\
\hline
\end{array}
$$

35.02 × 7 ≈ 245
The answer is reasonable.

$$
\begin{array}{r}
35.02 \\
\times7 \\
\hline
245.14 \\
\hline
\end{array}
$$

Primary Mathematics (Standards Edition) Extra Practice 4

Division

We divide decimals in the same way as whole numbers.

1. Divide 7.2 by 8.

    We align the decimal points.

    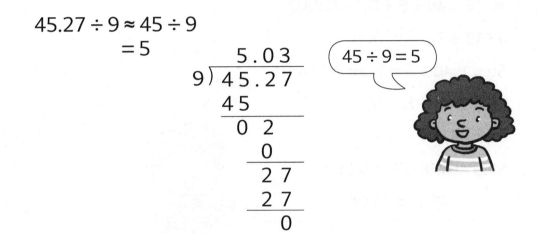
```
        0.9
    8) 7.2
       7 2
         0
```

2. Estimate the value. Then divide.

    $$45.27 \div 9 \approx 45 \div 9$$
    $$= 5$$

    $45 \div 9 = 5$

```
         5.0 3
    9) 4 5 . 2 7
       4 5
         0 2
           0
           2 7
           2 7
             0
```

3. Find the value of $24.6 \div 4$.

```
          6.1 5
    4) 2 4 . 6 0
       2 4
         0 6
           4
           2 0
           2 0
             0
```

$24.6 \div 4 = 6.15$

4. Find the value of $48.18 \div 3$.

$48.18 \div 3 = \$16.06$

$$
\begin{array}{r}
1\ 6.0\ 6 \\
3\overline{\smash{)}4\ 8.1\ 8} \\
\underline{3} \\
1\ 8 \\
\underline{1\ 8} \\
0\ 1\ 8 \\
\underline{1\ 8} \\
0
\end{array}
$$

$48.18 = 40 + 8 + 0.1 + 0.08$

$48.18 \div 3$:

Step 1: $40 \div 3 = 1$ ten $+ 10$ ones

Step 2: $10 + 8 = 18$

Step 3: $18 \div 3 = 6$

Step 4: $0.18 \div 3 = 0.06$

$48.18 = 16.06$

great Job!

Exercise 1 : Addition and Subtraction

1. Find the sum.

(a) $0.6 + 0.4 = 1.0$	(b) $0.7 + 0.8 = 1.5$
(c) $3.2 + 0.8 = 4.0$	(d) $5.4 + 0.9 = 6.3$
(e) $5.7 + 3 = 8.7$	(f) $7.6 + 2.9 = 10.5$
(g) $5.2 + 30.8 = 36.0$	(h) $2.6 + 29 = 31.6$
(i) $40.2 + 8.8 = 49.0$	(j) $356.4 + 9.7 = 366.1$
(k) $275.9 + 10.3 = 286.2$	(l) $240 + 61.4 = 301.4$

(m) $4.85 + 3.65 =$	(n) $3.46 + 0.8 =$
(o) $0.05 + 5.95 =$	(p) $23.16 + 0.08 =$
(q) $0.56 + 4.69 =$	(r) $1.8 + 0.74 =$
(s) $9.56 + 14.64 =$	(t) $51.8 + 7.34 =$
(u) $5.36 + 85.9 =$	(v) $3.4 + 43.58 =$
(w) $91.65 + 19 =$	(x) $1.06 + 369 =$

Primary Mathematics (Standards Edition) Extra Practice 4

2. Find the difference.

(a) $1.5 - 0.6 =$ 0.9 0 X. 5 c 6 9	(b) $3.1 - 1.3 =$ 2 3 1 1 1 . 3 ——— 1 . 8
(c) $9.4 - 8.6 =$ 8 9 . 1 4 8 . 6 ——— 0 . 8	(d) $7 - 3.4 = 3.6$ 6 7 . 1 0 3 . 4 ——— 3 . 6
(e) $5 - 0.5 =$ 4 5 . 1 0 0 . 5 ——— 4 . 5	(f) $8 - 0.1 =$ 7 8 1 0 0 1 7 . 9
(g) $1 - 0.5 =$ 9 1 0 5 . 5	(h) $28 - 0.8 =$ 2 8 . 1 0 -0.8 28 2 8 ——— 8 8 27.2 ——— ——— 20 20
(i) $70 - 0.1 =$ 6 7 0 . 1 0 6 7 0 . 1 0 0 0) ——— ——— 9 9 6 9 . 9	(j) $5.2 - 0.4 =$
(k) $7.03 - 6.8 =$	(l) $100 - 39.7 =$

3. Do these. Show all your work clearly.

   (a) Emma bought a storybook for $5.65 and a file for $4.80. She gave the cashier $20. How much change did she receive?

   (b) Tina is 1.53 m tall. She is 0.19 m shorter than her father. If her mother is 1.67 m tall, how much taller is her father than her mother?

(c) Tyrone weighs 30.3 kg. He is 3.45 kg heavier than his sister. What is their total weight?

(d) Caden bought a shirt and a belt. The shirt cost $14.75. The belt cost $6 more than the shirt. How much did he spend altogether?

(e)

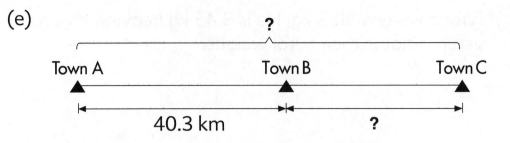

The distance from Town A to Town B is 40.3 km.
The distance from Town B to Town C is 3.95 km
shorter than the distance from Town A to Town B.
Find the distance from Town A to Town C.

(f) String A is 0.8 m longer than String B. String B is
0.75 m shorter than String C. If String C is 4 m, find the
total length of the three strings.

Exercise 2 : Multiplication

1. Find the products. Show your work clearly.

(a) 7 × 0.9 =	(b) 6 × 0.7 =
(c) 0.04 × 9 =	(d) 0.07 × 6 =

2. Find the products. Show your work clearly.

(a) 6.7 × 3 =	(b) 9 × 20.6 =
(c) 25.75 × 4 =	(d) 9 × 56.08 =

3. Write the amount of money in each set.

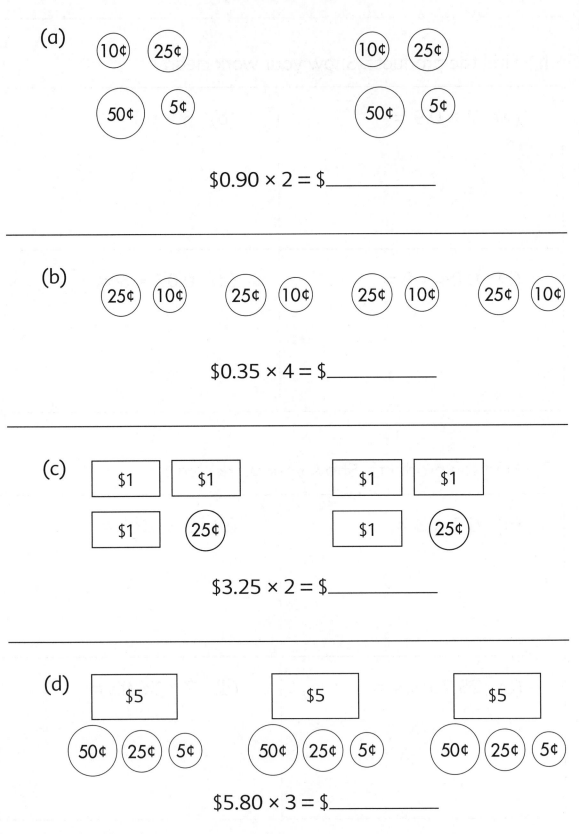

(a)

$0.90 × 2 = $_____

(b)

$0.35 × 4 = $_____

(c)

$3.25 × 2 = $_____

(d)

$5.80 × 3 = $_____

Primary Mathematics (Standards Edition) Extra Practice 4

4. Multiply.

(a)
$$\begin{array}{r} \$0.55 \\ \times\ \ \ \ 3 \\ \hline \\ \hline \end{array}$$

(b)
$$\begin{array}{r} \$2.25 \\ \times\ \ \ \ 4 \\ \hline \\ \hline \end{array}$$

(c)
$$\begin{array}{r} \$3.70 \\ \times\ \ \ \ 7 \\ \hline \\ \hline \end{array}$$

(d)
$$\begin{array}{r} \$4.05 \\ \times\ \ \ \ 9 \\ \hline \\ \hline \end{array}$$

(e)
$$\begin{array}{r} \$7.65 \\ \times\ \ \ \ 8 \\ \hline \\ \hline \end{array}$$

(f)
$$\begin{array}{r} \$9.20 \\ \times\ \ \ \ 10 \\ \hline \\ \hline \end{array}$$

5. Do these. Show all your work clearly.

(a) Joe bought 3 storybooks. Each book cost $4.65. How much did he pay altogether?

(b) Adam saved $0.85 each day for 6 days. If he gave his sister $1.25, how much money did he have left?

(c) Mrs. Hong bought 3 bath towels at $8.75 each.
     If she gave the cashier $40, how much change did
     she receive?

(d) Kate saved $15.35. John saved 4 times as much as
     Kate. How much did they save altogether?

(e) Jackie spent $3.15 on a diary and $0.80 on a piece of
     wrapping paper to prepare a gift.
     How much would it cost her to prepare 7 such gifts?

Primary Mathematics (Standards Edition) Extra Practice 4

Exercise 3 : Division

1. Find the quotients in decimals.

(a) $0.85 \div 5 =$	(b) $0.72 \div 6 =$
(c) $0.96 \div 8 =$	(d) $0.9 \div 5 =$
(e) $0.7 \div 2 =$	(f) $8.4 \div 3 =$
(g) $16.8 \div 8 =$	(h) $48.8 \div 4 =$
(i) $40.5 \div 9 =$	(j) $60.2 \div 7 =$

2. Find the quotient. Show your work clearly.

(a) $7.56 \div 3 =$	(b) $8.45 \div 5 =$
(c) $39.41 \div 7 =$	(d) $68.22 \div 9 =$

3. Divide. Give your answers in decimals. Show your work clearly.

(a) $3 \div 4 =$	(b) $7.3 \div 5 =$
(c) $50.8 \div 8 =$	(d) $51 \div 6 =$

4. Divide. Give each answer correct to 1 decimal place.
    Show your work clearly.

(a) $15.6 \div 5 =$	(b) $23.04 \div 4 =$
(c) $20.82 \div 3 =$	(d) $41.04 \div 6 =$
(e) $64.56 \div 8 =$	(f) $21.9 \div 8 =$
(g) $38.3 \div 9 =$	(h) $123 \div 4 =$

5. Find the amount.

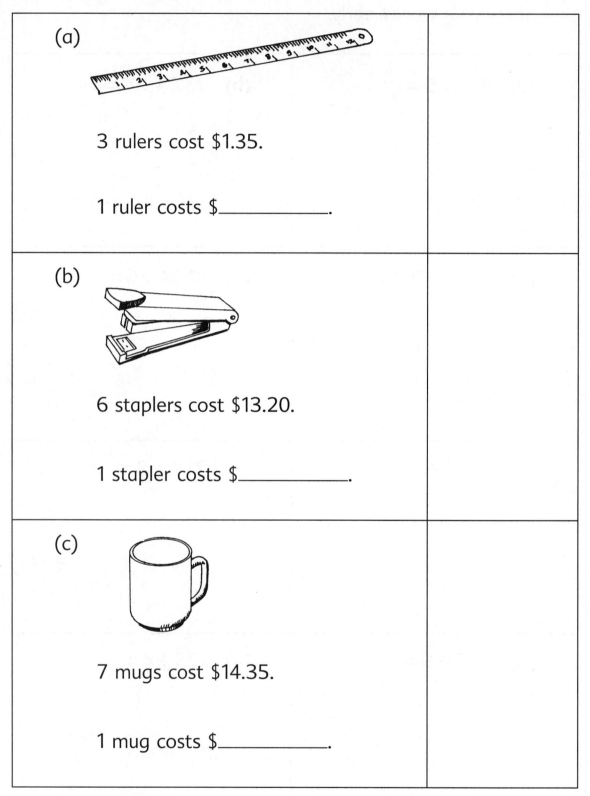

(a)

3 rulers cost $1.35.

1 ruler costs $_____.

(b)

6 staplers cost $13.20.

1 stapler costs $_____.

(c)

7 mugs cost $14.35.

1 mug costs $_____.

Primary Mathematics (Standards Edition) Extra Practice 4

6. Do these. Show all your work clearly.

(a) Kimberly shared $1.80 equally among her 4 nephews. How much money did each nephew get?

(b) Zhenni saved $2.50 in 10 days.
If she saved an equal amount of money each day, how much did she save in one day?

(c) Mrs. King had 5 purses.
Each purse contained $10.35.
If she divided the money equally among her 3 daughters, how much money did each daughter get?

(d) Catherine cut a ribbon 3.12 yd long into 4 equal pieces.
She used 3 pieces to tie some packages.
How many yards of ribbon did she use?

(e) Larry mixed 1.75 ℓ of orange juice with 5 times as
much water. He then poured the drink equally into
5 containers. How much drink was there in each
container?

(f) Karen paid $50.10 for 6 m of cloth and 2 pillows.
Each pillow cost $7.50. What was the cost of 1 m
of cloth?

Unit 8 : Congruent and Symmetric Figures

Congruent Figures

Two shapes are **congruent** if they are of the same size and shape. Congruent shapes fit each other exactly.

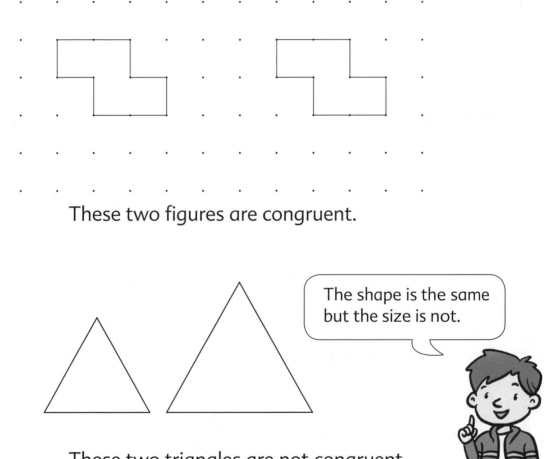

These two figures are congruent.

The shape is the same but the size is not.

These two triangles are not congruent.

Primary Mathematics (Standards Edition) Extra Practice 4

Tiling Patterns

Tiling patterns are made with congruent shapes. There are no gaps or overlaps between the shapes.

These tiling patterns are called **tessellations**.
The unit shape used is shaded.

(a)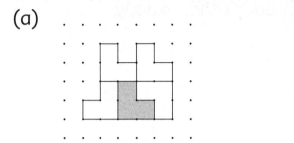

(b)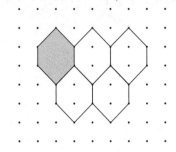

All quadrilaterals can tessellate.

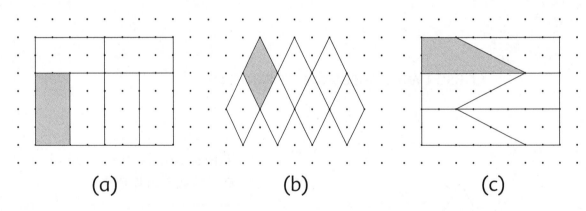

(a)   (b)   (c)

A circle cannot tessellate.

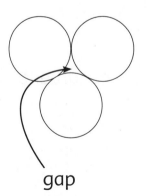 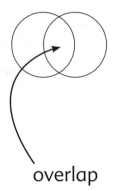

gap   overlap

Primary Mathematics (Standards Edition) Extra Practice 4   © 2008 Marshall Cavendish International (Singapore) Private Limited

Line Symmetry

A symmetric figure has one or more lines of symmetry.
A **line of symmetry** divides a figure into two equal parts.
These equal parts fit exactly.

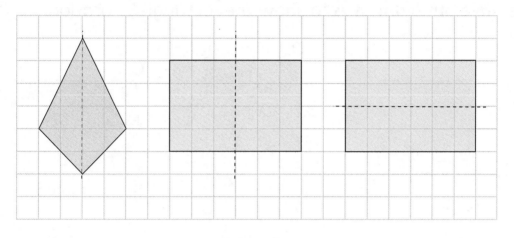

Each of the above figures has one line of symmetry.

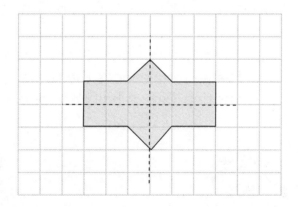

The figure above has more than one line of symmetry.

Rotational Symmetry

A figure has **rotational symmetry** if, after rotating less than 360°, the figure appears to be in the original position.

We have put a dot at A to show the rectangle's rotation.

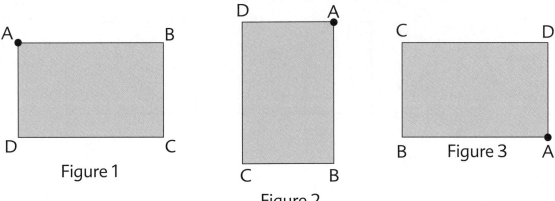

Figure 1

Figure 2

Figure 3

We can see that other than the dot, Figure 1 and Figure 3 look the same.

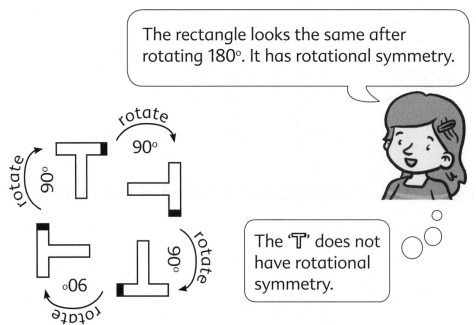

The rectangle looks the same after rotating 180°. It has rotational symmetry.

The 'T' does not have rotational symmetry.

Exercise 1 : Congruent Figures

1. Draw a figure that is congruent to each given figure.

(a)

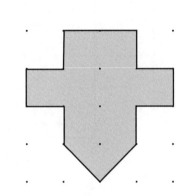

(b)

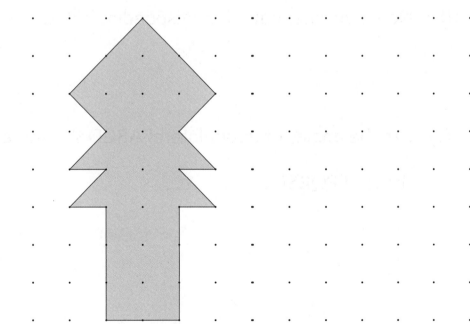

Primary Mathematics (Standards Edition) Extra Practice 4

2. Quadrilateral ABCD is congruent to quadrilateral PQRS.

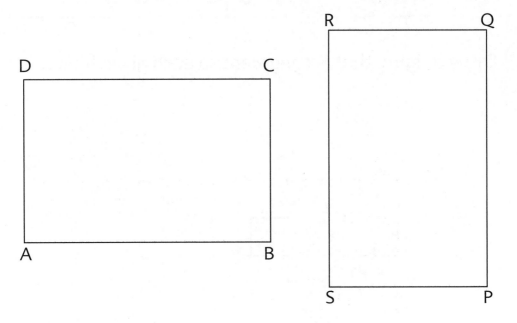

(a) Which side of quadrilateral ABCD does PQ correspond

to? _____

(b) Name another pair of corresponding sides.

_____

(c) Are the angles of quadrilateral ABCD the same as

those of PQRS? _____

Primary Mathematics (Standards Edition) Extra Practice 4

Exercise 2 : Tiling Patterns

1. Color the unit shape used in each of the following tessellations.

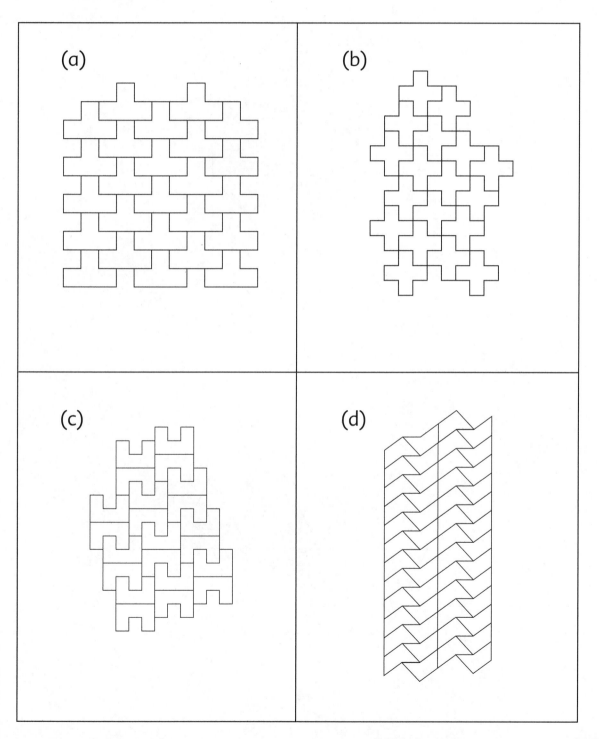

(a)

(b)

(c)

(d)

2. Extend each of the following tessellations in the space provided by drawing 5 more unit shapes.

(a)

(b)

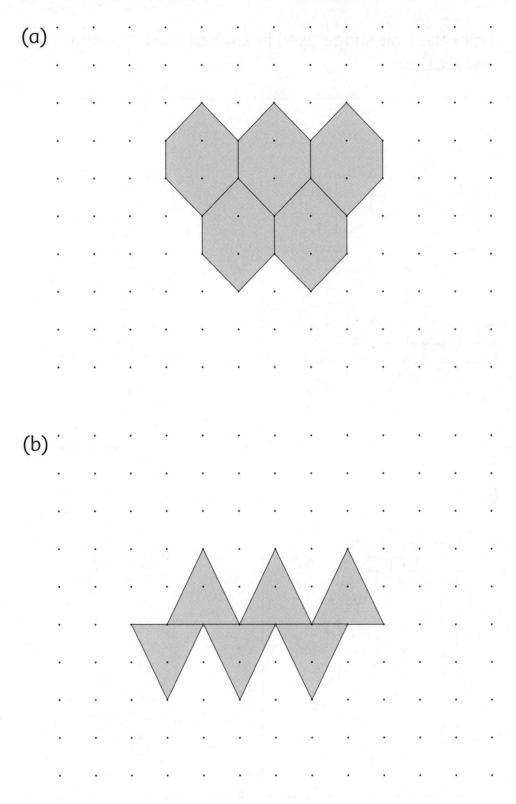

(c)

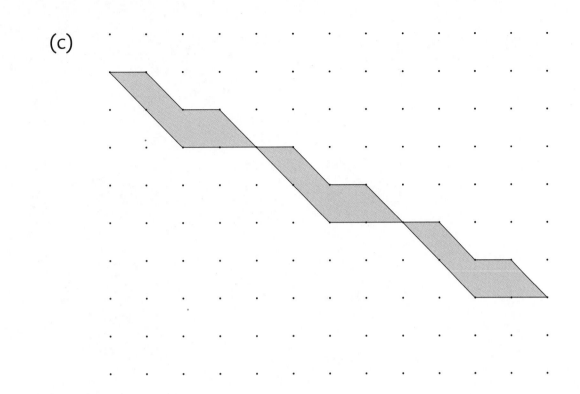

3. Use the given shape to make a tessellation in the space provided.

(a)

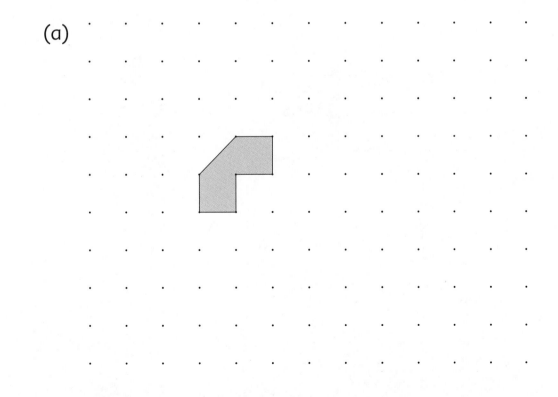

(b)

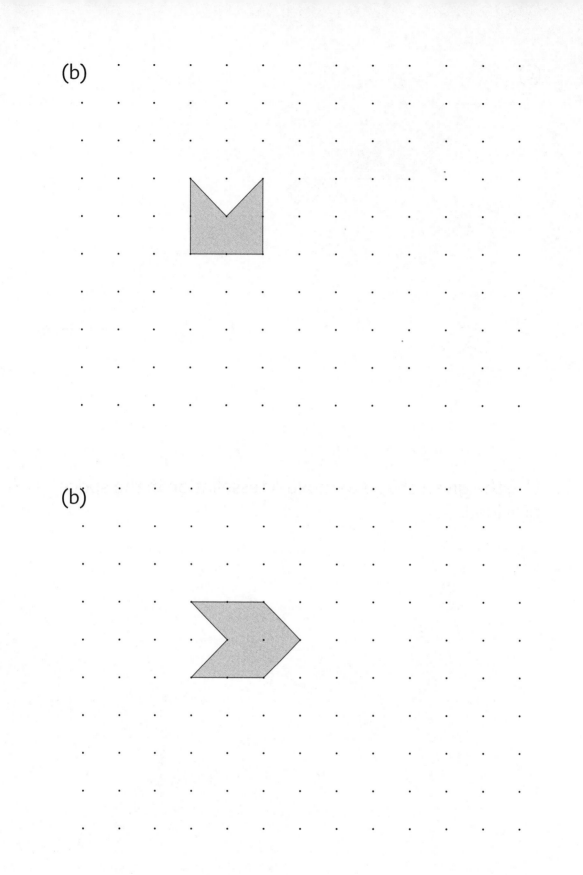

(b)

Exercise 3 : Line Symmetry

1. In each of the following figures, is the dotted line a line of symmetry? Write 'Yes' or 'No' in the blanks.

(a)

(b)

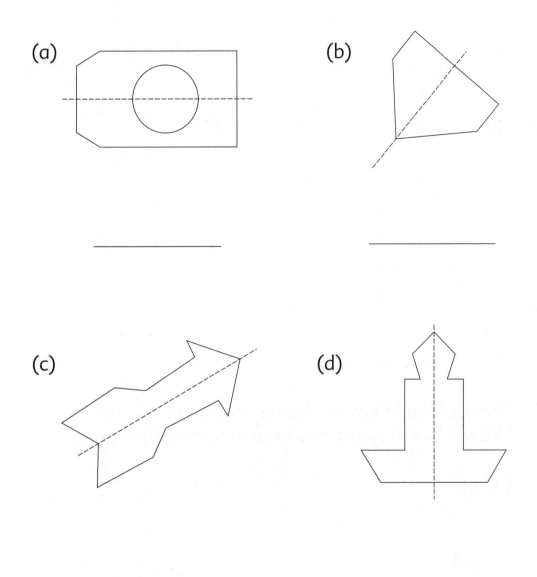

_____   _____

(c)

(d)

_____   _____

(e)

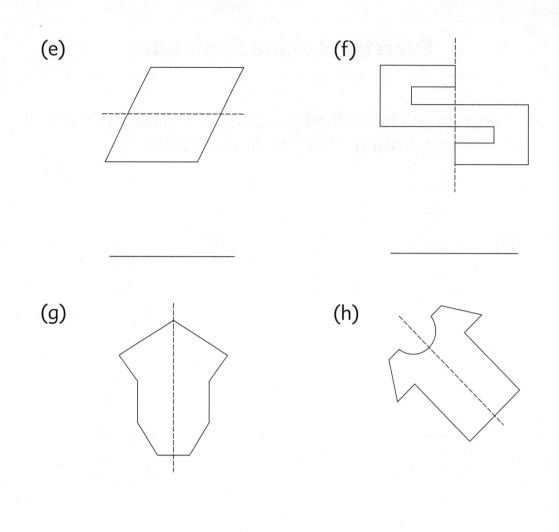

_____

(f)

_____

(g)

_____

(h)

_____

2. Some of the following figures are symmetric figures.
   Draw a line of symmetry in each symmetric figure.

(a)

(b)

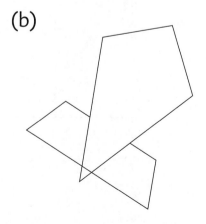

(c) (d)

(e) (f)

(g) (h)

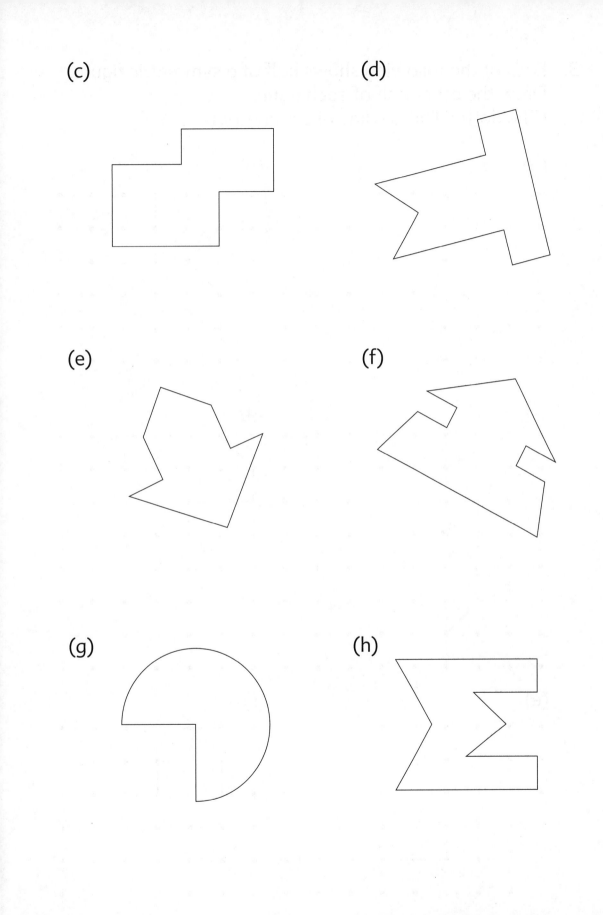

3. Each of the following shows half of a symmetric figure.
    Draw the other half of each figure.
    (The dotted line is a line of symmetry.)

(a)   (b)

(c)   (d)

(e)   (f)

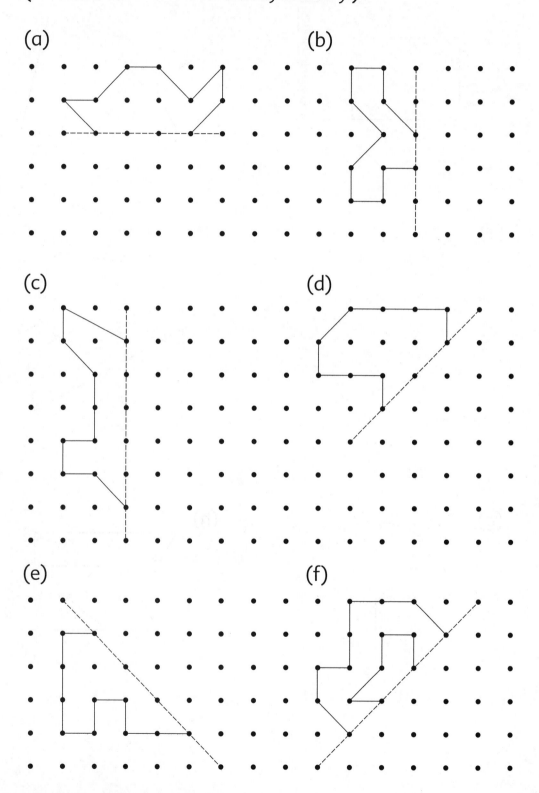

Exercise 4 : Rotational Symmetry

1. Check (✔) the boxes if the following figures have rotational symmetry.

   (a)

   (b)

   (c)

   (d)

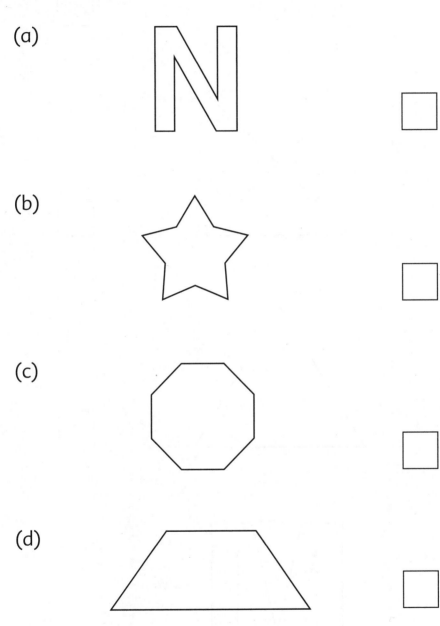

(e)

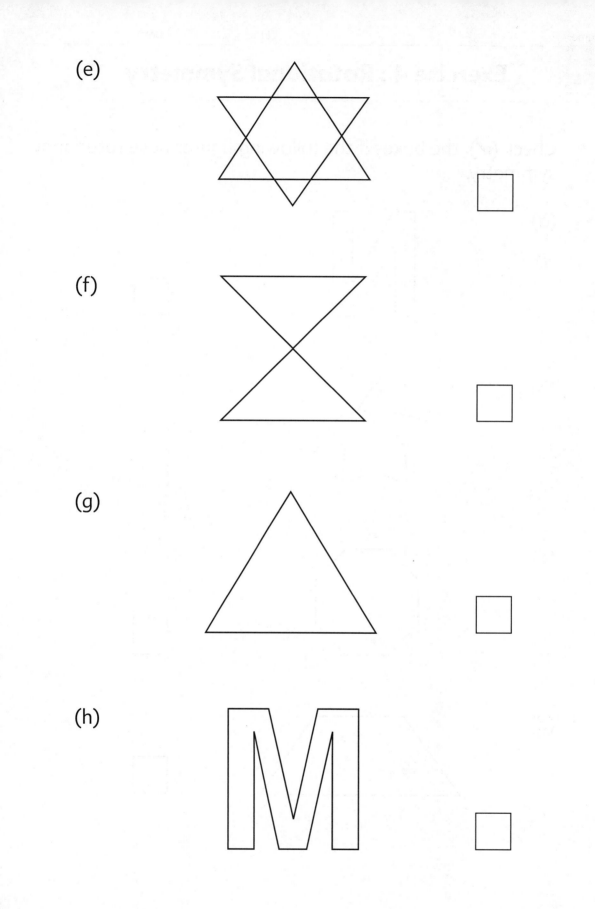

(f)

(g)

(h)

Unit 9 : Coordinate Graphs and Changes in Quantities

Friendly Notes

The Coordinate Grid

A coordinate grid has two axes. They are the horizontal axis and the vertical axis. The axes meet at the origin or the point (0, 0).

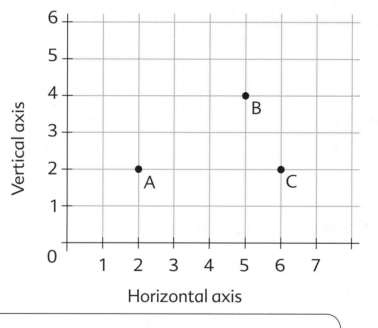

(2, 2) ⟶ two units from O along the horizontal and the vertical axes.

(5, 4) ⟶ five units from O along the horizontal axis, 4 units from O along the vertical axis.

(2, 2), (5, 4), and (6, 2) are **ordered pairs**.
The numbers in an ordered pair are called the **coordinates**.
Coordinates of A are (2, 2).
Coordinates of B are (5, 4).
Coordinates of C are (6, 2).

Changes in Quantities

When different quantities are related by an equation, a change in one quantity will affect the other quantities in the equation.

Recall that the formula for area of a rectangle is length × width. If either the length or the width changes, then the area of the rectangle will also change.

Suppose the length of a rectangle is twice its width.
If its length is 2 cm, its width is 1 cm and its area is 2 cm².
If its length is 4 cm, its width is 2 cm and its area is 8 cm², and so on as shown in the table below.

Length (L)	2 cm	4 cm	6 cm
Width (W)	1 cm	2 cm	3 cm
Area (A)	2 cm²	8 cm²	18 cm²

Graphing Changes in Quantity

We can draw a graph to show how a change in one quantity affects another quantity.

Using the values in the table above, we can draw a graph as follows:

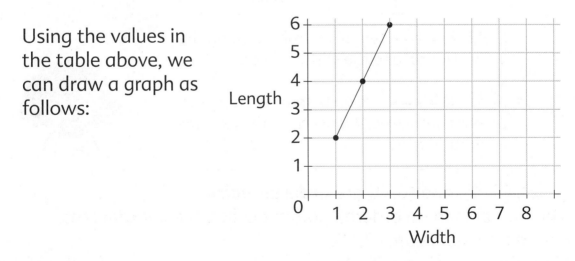

We get a straight line when we join the points.

Primary Mathematics (Standards Edition) Extra Practice 4

Exercise 1 : The Coordinate Grid

1. Give the ordered pair for each of the following points on the grid.

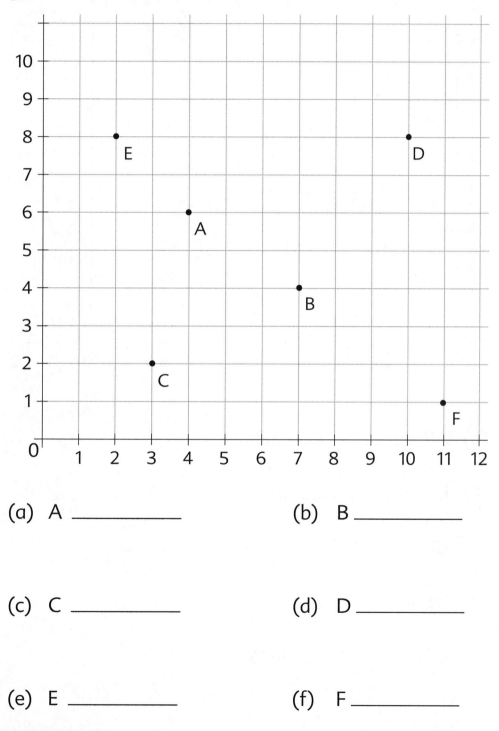

(a) A _____

(b) B _____

(c) C _____

(d) D _____

(e) E _____

(f) F _____

2. Find the length of each line segment.

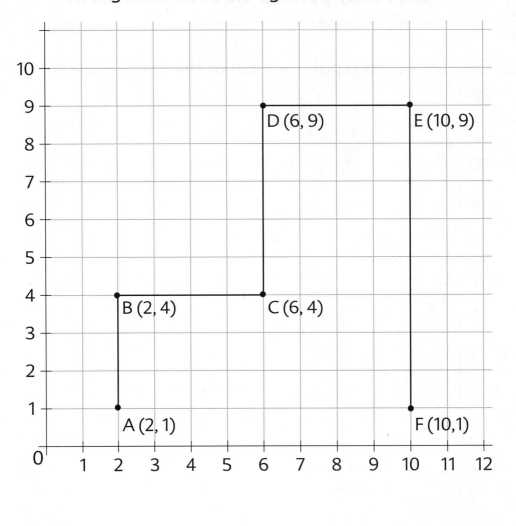

(a) AB = _____ units

(b) BC = _____ units

(c) CD = _____ units

(d) DE = _____ units

(e) EF = _____ units

Exercise 2 : Changes in Quantities

1. The length of a rectangle is three times its width. Find the change in its width as its length changes.

   (a) When its length is 9 cm, its width is _____ cm.

   (b) When its length is 12 cm, its width is _____ cm.

   (c) When its length is 21 cm, its width is _____ cm.

2. Complete the table and graph.
   (a)

Number of cakes	2	4	6	8	10
Total cost of cakes in dollars	10	20			50

   (b)

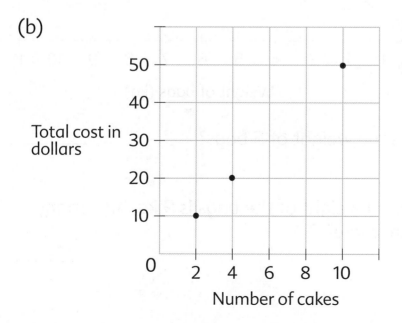

3. The graph shows the relationship between the weight and number of bags.

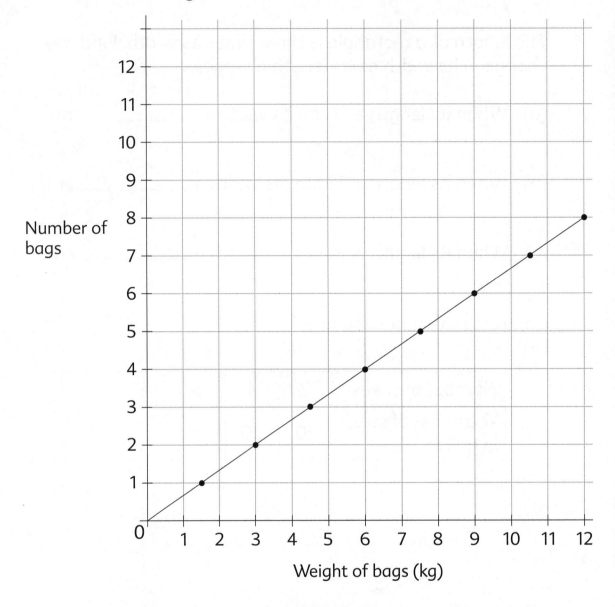

Number of bags

Weight of bags (kg)

(a) What is the weight of 5 bags? _____

(b) If the total weight of the bags is 9 kg, how many bags are there?

_____

Primary Mathematics (Standards Edition) Extra Practice 4

© 2008 Marshall Cavendish International (Singapore) Private Limited

Unit 10 : Data Analysis and Probability

Organizing and Analyzing Data

The results of surveys can be organized in different ways to help us analyze the data more easily. For example, we can organize the data from the least value to the largest value or we can use a line plot to present the data. The middle number of a set of data is called the **median**. The value that appears most often in a set of data is the **mode** of the data. There can be more than one mode.

A survey was conducted to find the number of fruits 20 students eat in a day. The data collected is recorded in the tally chart.

Number of fruits eaten	Tally
0	////
1	##### /
2	##### //
3	///

We organize the data from least to most.

0, 0, 0, 0, 1, 1, 1, 1, 1, 1, 2, 2, 2, 2, 2, 2, 2, 3, 3, 3

middle
numbers

$$\text{Median} = \frac{1+2}{2} = 1.5$$

Mode $= 2$
The data is shown on a line plot as follows:

Number of fruits eaten

Probability Experiments

We can conduct **probability experiments** to determine the probability of an outcome.

Order of Outcomes

A tree diagram is used to show the possible outcomes of an experiment.

Suppose a bag contains red balls, green balls and blue balls. Two balls are drawn from the bag each time.

The tree diagram below shows the possible outcomes of the experiment.

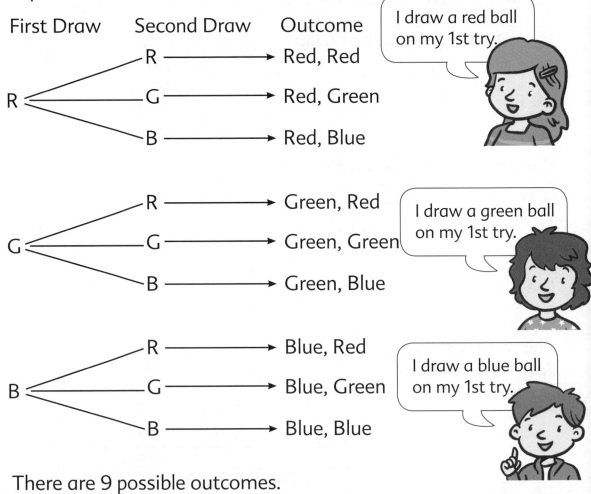

There are 9 possible outcomes.

Bar Graphs

A **bar graph** makes comparison of data easy.

The table below shows the number of people who went to a concert during a week.

Day	Number of people
Monday	500
Tuesday	1500
Wednesday	1000
Thursday	1000
Friday	2500
Saturday	4500
Sunday	6000

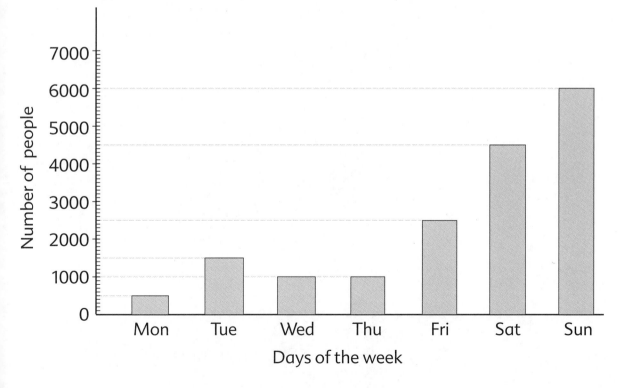

Primary Mathematics (Standards Edition) Extra Practice 4

Line Graphs

We can present data using a **line graph**.

Using the same set of data as that of the bar graph, we can draw a line graph as follows.

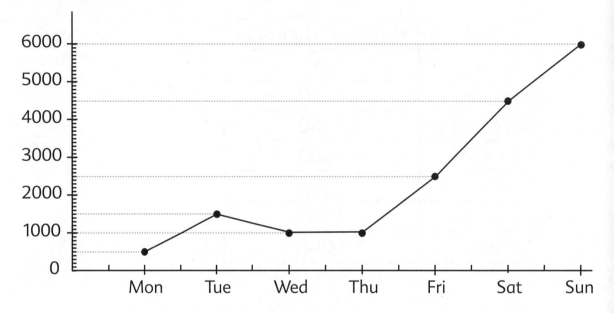

Primary Mathematics (Standards Edition) Extra Practice 4

© 2008 Marshall Cavendish International (Singapore) Private Limited

Exercise 1 : Organizing and Analyzing Data

1. Study the tally chart and answer the questions that follow.

Number of children in a family	Tally
0	///
1	//// //
2	//// /
3	//// /
4	//// ///

(a) How many families have no children? _____

(b) What is the greatest number of children shown in the tally chart?

_____

(c) How many families are there altogether? _____

2. (a) Use the data shown in the tally chart on page 157 to plot a line graph.

(b) What is the mode?

Exercise 2 : Probability Experiments

1. There are green, red and blue balls in a bag. Jack drew 5 balls from a bag each time.

   The line plot shows the number of green balls drawn on 5 tries each time.

   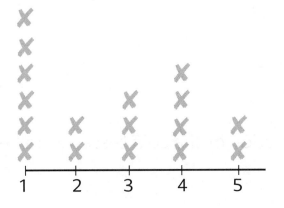

   (a) How many times did he draw only 1 green ball for every 5 tries?

   _____

   (b) How many times did he draw 4 green balls for every 5 tries?

   _____

   (c) How many 5 tries did Jack attempt?

   _____

2. Linda tossed a coin 15 times. She obtained 10 heads and 5 tails.

    (a) Linda obtained tails _____ out of _____ times.

    (b) What fraction of the coin tosses were tails?

         _____

    (c) What fraction of the coin tosses were heads?

         _____

Exercise 3 : Order of Outcomes

1. There are red, blue and yellow marbles in a bag. Susie draws out two marbles, one marble at a time. What are the possible outcomes?

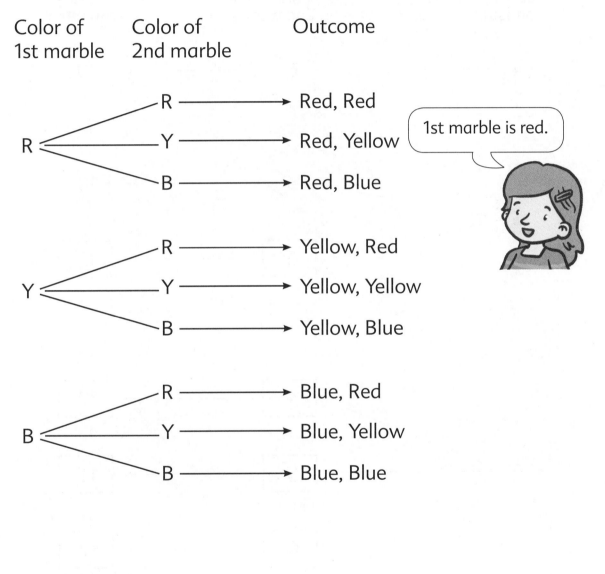

Color of
1st marble

Color of
2nd marble

Outcome

R ⟶ Red, Red

R ⟨ Y ⟶ Red, Yellow

B ⟶ Red, Blue

1st marble is red.

R ⟶ Yellow, Red

Y ⟨ Y ⟶ Yellow, Yellow

B ⟶ Yellow, Blue

R ⟶ Blue, Red

B ⟨ Y ⟶ Blue, Yellow

B ⟶ Blue, Blue

There are _____ possible outcomes.

Primary Mathematics (Standards Edition) Extra Practice 4

2. Complete the tree diagram.

   Jebsen tossed a regular die twice. What are the possible outcomes of getting a sum that is greater than 9?

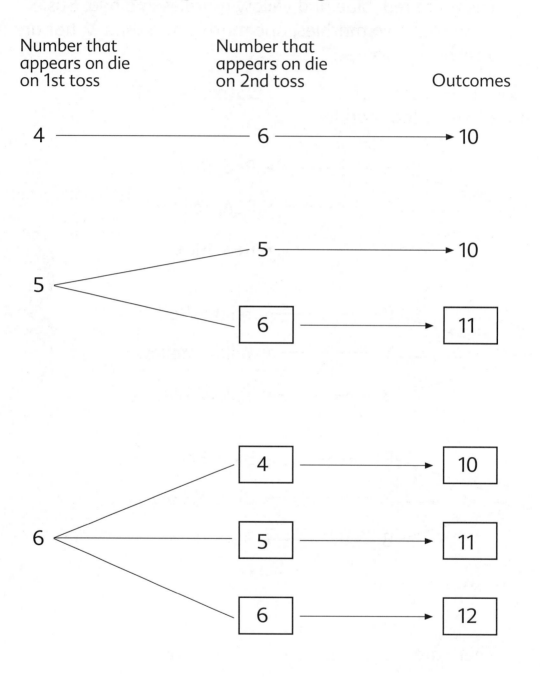

© 2008 Marshall Cavendish International (Singapore) Private Limited

Exercise 4 : Bar Graphs

1. The bar graph shows the number of tickets sold at a cinema in a week. Study the graph and answer the questions which follow.

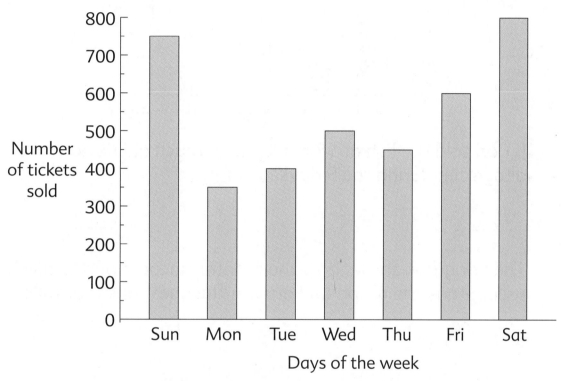

Days of the week

(a) What is the total number of tickets sold on Saturday and Sunday? _____

(b) How many tickets were sold from Monday to Friday? _____

(c) How many more tickets were sold on Friday than on Monday? _____

(d) On Saturday, if 265 tickets were sold at $8.00 each and the rest at $6.00 each, how much money did the cinema collect in all? _____

2. The graph below shows the weight of fish sold by Carl in 5 days. Study the graph and answer the question that follows.

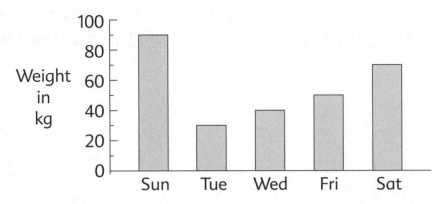

If Carl sold the fish at $8 per kg, how much did he earn altogether during the 5 days?

_____

3. The bar graph shows how the monthly income of a family is used. Study the graph and answer the questions that follow.

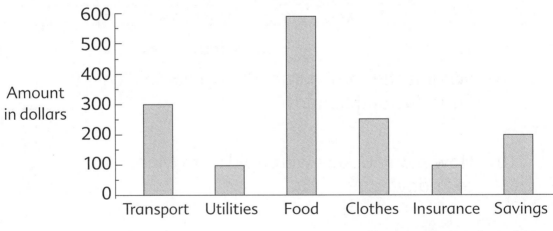

(a) What is the total monthly expenditure of the family?

_____

(b) What is the total monthly income of the family if $\frac{1}{9}$ of the total income is spent on food?

_____

Exercise 5 : Line Graphs

1. Study the line graph and answer the questions that follow.

    The table shows the daily sales of hot dogs at a hot dog stand.

Mon	Tue	Wed	Thu	Fri	Sat	Sun
45	50	60	65	70	80	100

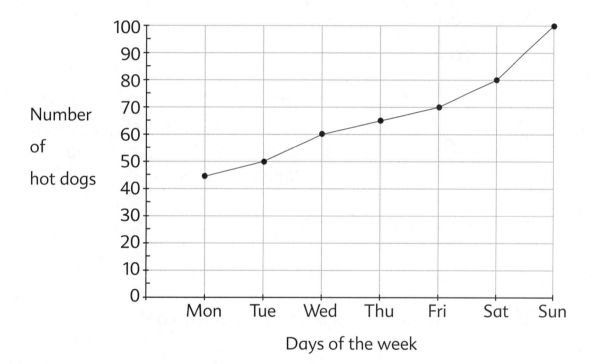

(a) On which day were the sales of hot dogs the highest?

_____

(b) What was the increase in sales in hot dogs between Friday and Saturday?

_____

2. The line graph shows the prices of different numbers of toys. Use it to answer the questions that follow.

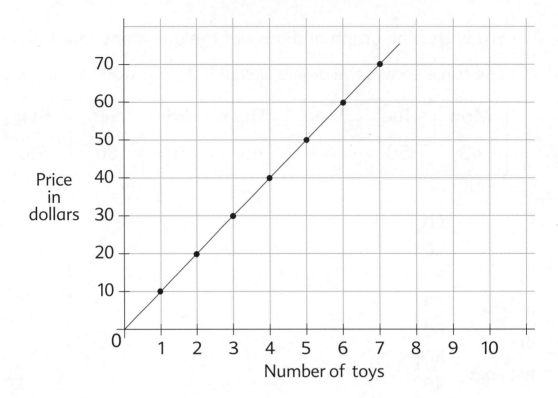

(a) Find the cost of 6 toys.

(b) What should the cost of 20 such toys be?

(c) Sulin paid $80 for some of those toys. How many toys did she buy?

Primary Mathematics (Standards Edition) Extra Practice 4   © 2008 Marshall Cavendish International (Singapore) Private Limited

Unit 11 : Measures and Volume

Friendly Notes

Adding and Subtracting Measures

Conversion of Measurements

Length:
1 m = 100 cm
1 km = 1000 m
1 yd = 3 ft
1 ft = 12 in.

Weight:
1 kg = 1000 g
1 lb = 16 oz

Capacity:
1 ℓ = 1000 ml
1 gal = 4 qt
1 qt = 2 pt
1 pt = 2 c

Time:
1 year = 12 months
1 week = 7 days
1 day = 24 hours
1 hour = 60 minutes
1 minute = 60 seconds

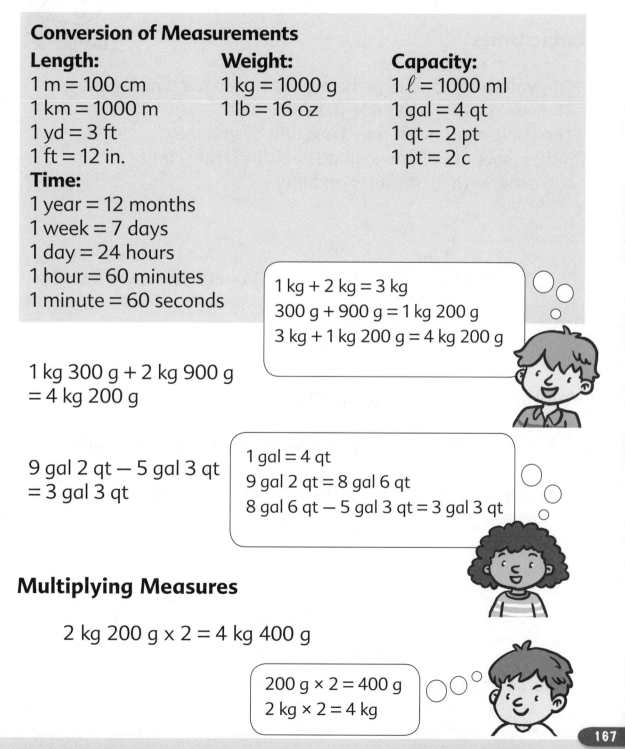

1 kg 300 g + 2 kg 900 g
= 4 kg 200 g

> 1 kg + 2 kg = 3 kg
> 300 g + 900 g = 1 kg 200 g
> 3 kg + 1 kg 200 g = 4 kg 200 g

9 gal 2 qt − 5 gal 3 qt
= 3 gal 3 qt

> 1 gal = 4 qt
> 9 gal 2 qt = 8 gal 6 qt
> 8 gal 6 qt − 5 gal 3 qt = 3 gal 3 qt

Multiplying Measures

2 kg 200 g x 2 = 4 kg 400 g

> 200 g × 2 = 400 g
> 2 kg × 2 = 4 kg

167

Dividing Measures

6 m 25 cm ÷ 5 = 1 m 25 cm

6 m ÷ 5 = 1 m remainder 1 m
1 m = 100 cm
100 cm + 25 cm = 125 cm
125 cm ÷ 5 = 25 cm

Cubic Units

The **volume** of a solid is the amount of space it occupies.
The volume of a unit cube is 1 cubic unit.
The cubic centimeter (cm^3) is a unit of volume.
Other units of volume include cubic inch (in.^{3}) and
cubic meter (m^3), milliliter and liter.

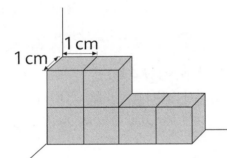

Volume of solid = 6 cm^3

Volume of a Rectangular Prism

Volume of a rectangular prism = Length × Width × Height

A rectangular prism measures 5 cm by 2 cm by 3 cm.

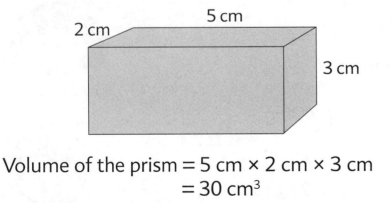

Volume of the prism = 5 cm × 2 cm × 3 cm
= 30 cm^3

Exercise 1 : Adding and Subtracting Measures

1. Fill in the blanks.

   (a) 5 kg 300 g + 3 kg = _____

   (b) 12 lb 10 oz + 6 lb = _____

   (c) 20 kg 800 g − 5 kg = _____

   (d) 35 gal 2 qt − 6 gal = _____

2. Find the missing numbers.

   (a) 30 ft 10 in. + 18 ft 6 in. = _____ ft _____ in.

   (b) 23 min 45 s + 12 min 22 s = _____ min _____ s

   (c) 19 gal 2 qt − 5 gal 3 qt = _____ gal _____ qt

   (d) 11 lb 6 oz − 6 lb 12 oz = _____ lb _____ oz

   (e) 1 ft − 8 in. = _____ in.

   (f) 1 lb − 8 oz = _____ oz

3. Write the correct answer.

(a) The total weight of 2 mangoes is 4 kg. The smaller mango weighs $1\frac{1}{2}$ kg. What is the weight of the other mango?

_____

(b) Container A has 2 ℓ 500 ml of water. Container B has 6 ℓ 350 ml of water. How much more water does Container B have than Container A?

_____

Exercise 2 : Multiplying Measures

1. Multiply in compound units.

   (a) 5 km 600 m × 7

   (b) 10 yd 3 ft × 5

   (c) 12 ℓ 750 ml × 8

   (d) 3 h 42 min × 9

2. Do these. Show all your work clearly.

    (a) Ryan saved $84 in 6 weeks. If he saved an equal amount each week, how much would he save in 26 weeks?

    (b) A boy ran 8 times round a rectangular field measuring 52 m by 30 m. What was the distance he ran?

(c) James weighs 52 kg 700 g. He is twice as heavy as his sister. Find their total weight.

(d) The capacity of Tank A is 4 gal 3 qt. The capacity of Tank B is 3 times that of Tank A. What is the total capacity of the two tanks?

(e) Joshua spends 1 hour 35 minutes exercising every day.
     How much time does he spend exercising in a week?

(f) The length of one string is 2 ft 3 in. What is the total
     length of 4 such strings?

(g) The width of a rectangle is 1 m 15 cm. Its length is
     2 times its width. Find the perimeter of the rectangle.

Exercise 3 : Dividing Measures

1. Divide in compound units.

    (a) 8 m 48 cm ÷ 4

    (b) 6 ft 3 in. ÷ 3

    (c) 12 qt 6 pt ÷ 5

    (d) 25 years 6 months ÷ 6

2. Do these. Show all your work clearly.

    (a) A ribbon 5 m 40 cm long is cut into 5 equal pieces. How long is each piece?

    (b) John spent $4680 in 5 months. If he spent an equal amount each month, how much would he spend in a year?

(c) Mrs. Li used 2 packets of flour to bake 10 cakes.
Packet A contained 2 kg 250 g of flour. Packet B
contained 3 kg 900 g. If she used the same amount
of flour to bake each cake, how much flour did she use
for each cake?

(d) Morgan works 8 hours 30 minutes every day.
He is paid $5 per hour. If he earns $510, how many
days does he work?

(e) A painter mixed 8.5 liters of blue paint and 17.5 liters of yellow paint. After using 9.5 liters of the mixture, he poured the rest equally into 3 tins. How much paint was there in each tin?

(f) 12 pails of the same size were used to fill a tank with water. The capacity of the tank was 42 gallons. Find the capacity of each pail. Give your answer in gallons and quarts.

Exercise 4 : Cubic Units

1. How many cubic units are there?

(a)

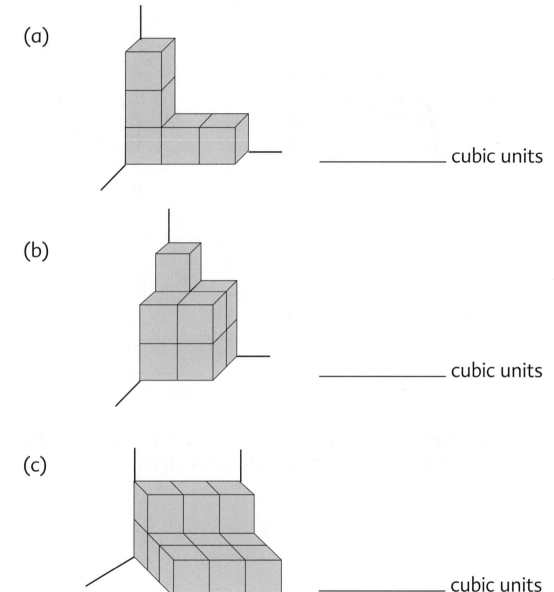

_____ cubic units

(b)

_____ cubic units

(c)

_____ cubic units

2. The following solids are made up of 1-cm cubes. Find the volume of each solid.

(a)

(b)

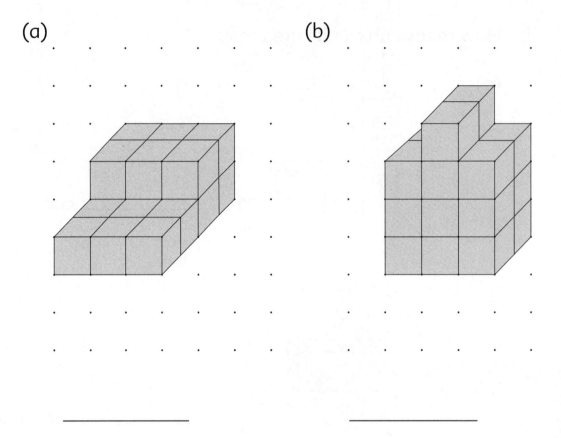

_____   _____

(c) How many more 1-cm cubes must be added to the solid in (a) so that its volume is 20 cm³?

_____

Primary Mathematics (Standards Edition) Extra Practice 4   © 2008 Marshall Cavendish International (Singapore) Private Limited

Exercise 5 : Volume of Rectangular Prisms

1. Fill in the blanks.

    The following rectangular prisms are made up of 1-cm cubes. Find the length, width, height and volume of each rectangular prism.

    (a)

    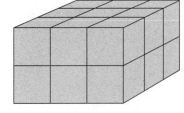

    Length = _____ cm

    Width = _____ cm

    Height = _____ cm

    Volume = _____ cm³

    (b)

    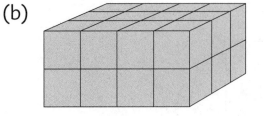

    Length = _____ cm

    Width = _____ cm

    Height = _____ cm

    Volume = _____ cm³

2. Find the volume of each rectangular prism. Show your work clearly.

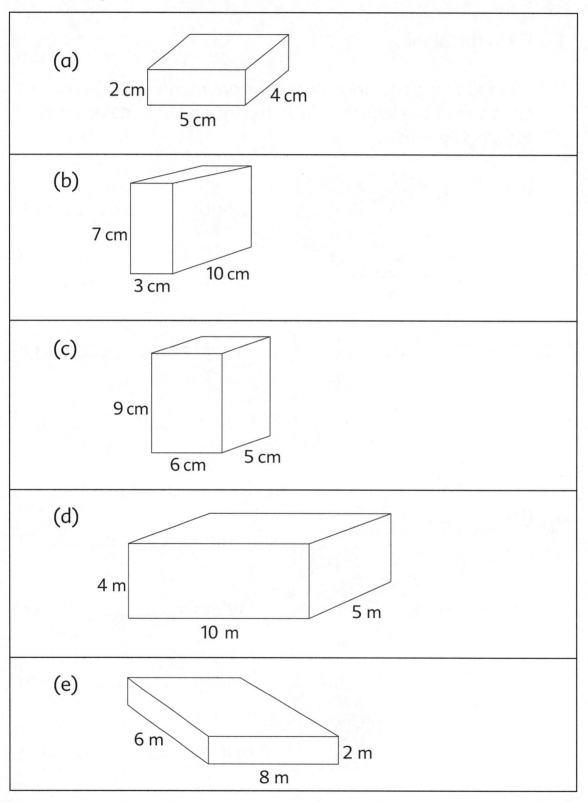

(a)

2 cm
4 cm
5 cm

(b)

7 cm
3 cm
10 cm

(c)

9 cm
6 cm
5 cm

(d)

4 m
10 m
5 m

(e)

6 m
8 m
2 m

Primary Mathematics (Standards Edition) Extra Practice 4

© 2008 Marshall Cavendish International (Singapore) Private Limited

ANSWERS

Unit 1 Whole Numbers

Exercise 1

1. (a) 27,005   (b) 250,600
   (c) 93,009   (d) 550,046

2. (a) 40,000 + 7000 + 500
   (b) 500,000 + 10,000 + 6000 + 200 + 40
   (c) 600,000 + 2000 + 80 + 3
   (d) 90,000 + 3000 + 5
   (e) 2,000,000 + 100,000 + 30,000
   (f) 8,000,000 + 10,000 + 5000

3. (a) Forty thousand, five hundred sixteen
   (b) Ten thousand, twenty
   (c) Two hundred thirteen thousand, four hundred
   (d) Five hundred two thousand, one
   (e) Three hundred thousand, two hundred eight
   (f) Five million, six thousand
   (g) Three hundred forty-eight million, seven hundred fifteen thousand, nine hundred eight

4. (a) 100   (b) thousands, 3000
   (c) ten thousands, 20,000
   (d) 200,000   (e) 5,000,000   (f) 7, 2

5. (a) 35,206   (b) 428,007
   (c) 600   (d) 70,000

6. (a) 49,326   (b) 600
   (c) 171,000   (d) 1,351,979

7. (a) 25,792, 25,822
   (b) 40,136, 40,236
   (c) 70,271, 73,271
   (d) 65,810, 70,810

8. (a) 16,538, 46,385, 130,568, 336,058
   (b) 104,002, 140,105, 1,165,305, 23,806,441

9. (a) 2, 6, 5, 4, 0, 1, 8, 9
   (b) 6, 9, 3, 2, 4, 0, 8, 5, 7

Exercise 2

1. (a) 570   (b) 1290   (c) 12,400
   (d) 107,410

2. (a) 4900   (b) 11,900   (c) 318,000
   (d) 1,564,100

3. (a) 22,000   (b) 107,000   (c) 742,000
   (d) 23,785,000

4. (a) 20,000   (b) 290,000
   (c) 1,450,000   (d) 106,470,000

5. (a) 100,000   (b) 7,200,000
   (c) 19,500,000   (d) 124,800,000

6. (a) 3,000,000   (b) 18,000,000
   (c) 390,000,000   (d) 539,000,000

7. $1,800,000

8. 29,000,000

Exercise 3

1. (a) 7   (b) 8   (c) 18   (d) 25

2. (a) 1, 2, 3, 6, 9, 18
   (b) 1, 3, 9, 27, 81
   (c) 1, 2, 4, 7, 8, 14, 28, 56
   (d) 1, 2, 7, 14, 49, 98

3. (a) 12, 20, 36   (b) 12, 27, 36
   (c) 20   (d) 11, 19
   (e) 12, 20, 27, 36

4. (a) 4   (b) 3
   (c) 12   (d) 9

5. (a) Yes   (b) 1, 2, 3, 6

Exercise 4

1. (a) 3, 6, 9, 12   (b) 5, 10, 15, 20
   (c) 7, 14, 21, 28   (d) 9, 18, 27, 36

2. (a) 18, 36   (b) 12, 24

3. (a) 32, 60, 72, 88   (b) 72

4. (a) 60   (b) 120

5. (a) 60, 75   (b) 27, 36, 45

Exercise 5

1. (a) 18   (b) 58   (c) 6
   (d) 14   (e) 26   (f) 123
   (g) 230   (h) 64

2. (a) 40   (b) $7.25

Exercise 6

1. (a) −1, −2, −3, −4, −5, −6
   (b) −1

2. (a) >   (b) <   (c) >
   (d) <   (e) >   (f) <

3. 100, 28, −19, −66, −91

4. (a) −20 °C   (b) −$1500   (c) −20 m

5. (a) −20   (b) −75   (c) −112   (d) −315

Primary Mathematics (Standards Edition) Extra Practice 4

Unit 2 The Four Operations of Whole Numbers

Exercise 1

1. (a) 2735   (b) 15,768
   (c) 3,027,064   (d) 20,148,123

2. (a) 52,422   (b) 7,884,896
   (c) 23,112,914   (d) 103,043,823

3. (a) 550   (b) 1563

4. (a) 183 dolls   (b) 629 more children

Exercise 2

1. (a) 536   (b) 4230
   (c) 55,032   (d) 20,272

2. (a) 56   (b) 906   (c) 738   (d) 563

3. (a) 26,736   (b) 161

Exercise 3

1. (a) 5040   (b) 51,120   (c) 1932
   (d) 40,000   (e) 62,426   (e) 23,414

2. (a) 2100   (b) 36,000

3. (a) 4235 g or 4 kg 235 g   (b) 804

Unit 3 Fractions

Exercise 1

1. (a) 2   (b) 4   (c) 15   (d) 9
   (e) 10   (f) 28

2. (a) 9   (b) 6   (c) 12   (d) 5
   (e) 5   (f) 7

3. (a) 3, 12, 9   (b) 15, 15, 40

4. (a) $\frac{3}{4}$ (b) $\frac{1}{4}$ (c) $\frac{2}{3}$ (d) $\frac{2}{3}$

5. (a) $\frac{10}{20}, \frac{7}{10}, \frac{4}{5}$ (b) $\frac{2}{3}, \frac{9}{12}, \frac{5}{6}$

6. (a) $\frac{5}{6}, \frac{2}{3}, \frac{5}{9}$ (b) $\frac{5}{6}, \frac{3}{4}, \frac{1}{2}$

7. (a) Dani
   (b) The melon is the heaviest.
   The papaya is the lightest.

Exercise 2

1. (a) $\frac{2}{5}$ (b) $\frac{5}{7}$ (c) $\frac{4}{5}$
   (d) $\frac{2}{3}$ (e) $\frac{7}{9}$ (f) 1

2. (a) $\frac{2}{6}, \frac{3}{6}$ or $\frac{1}{2}$ (b) $\frac{6}{8}, \frac{7}{8}$

3. (a) $\frac{3}{4}$ (b) $\frac{5}{6}$ (c) $\frac{3}{4}$
   (d) 1   (e) 1   (f) $\frac{5}{6}$

4. (a) $\frac{1}{2}$ (b) $\frac{2}{3}$ (c) $\frac{3}{5}$
   (d) $\frac{3}{4}$ (e) $\frac{3}{4}$ (f) $\frac{11}{12}$

5. (a) $\frac{2}{4}$ or $\frac{1}{2}$ (b) $\frac{1}{8}$

6. (a) $\frac{4}{6}, \frac{1}{2}$ or $\frac{3}{6}$ (b) $\frac{6}{8}, \frac{1}{8}$

7. (a) $\frac{1}{2}$ (b) $\frac{2}{5}$ (c) $\frac{3}{7}$
   (d) $\frac{1}{3}$ (e) $\frac{1}{5}$ (f) $\frac{1}{6}$

8. (a) $\frac{1}{6}$ (b) $\frac{1}{2}$ (c) $\frac{5}{9}$
   (d) $\frac{1}{2}$ (e) $\frac{1}{4}$ (f) $\frac{4}{5}$

9. (a) $\frac{1}{4}$ (b) $\frac{1}{5}$ (c) 0
   (d) $\frac{1}{3}$ (e) $\frac{1}{5}$ (f) $\frac{1}{2}$

10. (a) $\frac{3}{7}$ (b) $\frac{5}{8}$ ft   (c) John, $\frac{1}{4}$ more
    (d) $\frac{3}{4}$ (e) $\frac{7}{10}$ kg

Exercise 3

1. (a) $2\frac{1}{2}$ (b) $3\frac{2}{3}$ (c) $2\frac{3}{4}$
   (d) $7\frac{5}{8}$

2. (a) $2\frac{7}{8}$ (b) $3\frac{3}{4}$ (c) $1\frac{1}{3}$
   (d) $4\frac{3}{5}$

3. (a) $1\frac{1}{5}$ (b) $3\frac{1}{2}$ (c) $7\frac{1}{2}$
   (d) $4\frac{1}{3}$ (e) $3\frac{2}{5}$ (f) $6\frac{1}{7}$

4. (a) $2\frac{4}{5}$ yd   (b) $4\frac{1}{2}$ m

Exercise 4

1. (a) $\frac{10}{5}$ (b) $\frac{9}{4}$ (c) $\frac{18}{6}$
   (d) $\frac{11}{3}$

2. (a) 12   (b) 10   (c) 7
   (d) 7   (e) 5   (f) 11

3. (a) $1\frac{4}{5}$ (b) 3   (c) $3\frac{3}{4}$
   (d) $1\frac{9}{10}$

4. (a) $1\frac{2}{3}$ (b) $2\frac{5}{6}$ (c) $6\frac{1}{2}$
   (d) 9   (e) $8\frac{7}{12}$ (f) $14\frac{1}{3}$

5. (a) $\frac{11}{6}$ (b) $\frac{25}{9}$ (c) $\frac{39}{10}$
   (d) $\frac{55}{12}$ (e) $\frac{28}{5}$ (f) $\frac{105}{11}$

Exercise 5

1. $1\frac{1}{2}$

2. (a) $5\frac{1}{2}$ (b) $6\frac{1}{4}$

3. $\frac{3}{4}$

4. (a) $3\frac{1}{2}$ kg   (b) $22.50

Exercise 6

1. (a) 6   (b) 20   (c) 24
   (d) 35   (e) 96   (f) 112
   (g) 6   (h) 5

2. (a) $\frac{2}{5}$ (b) $\frac{3}{5}$ (c) $\frac{3}{4}$

   (d) $\frac{7}{20}$ (e) $\frac{2}{3}$ (f) $\frac{1}{4}$

3. (a) 28   (b) 16   (c) $\frac{1}{3}$

   (d) $\frac{3}{5}$ (e) $\frac{1}{5}$ (f) $\frac{1}{4}$

Unit 4 Geometry

Exercise 1

1. (a)

There are 3 right angles.

(b)

There are 2 right angles.

(c)

There are 4 right angles.

(d)

There are 2 right angles.

2. (a) school   (b) tree   (c) hill
   (d) school   (e) bus stop   (f) tree
   (g) school

Exercise 2

1. (a) a, b, c, d, h, k, q, y, z
   (b) e, f, o, p, n, r, u, v, x
   (c) g, i, j, l, m, s, t, w

2. (a) 45°   (b) 90°   (c) 120°
   (d) 105°   (e) 67°   (f) 157°

3.

∠a = 75°

∠b = 38°

∠c = 70°

∠d = 165°

∠e = 123°

∠f = 136°

4. (a) 50°   (b) 25°   (c) 34°   (d) 55°

5. (a) 38°   (b) 108°

6. (a) 4, 360   (b) 2, 180   (c) 1, 90   (d) 3, 270

7. (a) 220°   (b) 310°   (c) 245°   (d) 335°

Exercise 3

1. (a) AE ⊥ AB, ED ⊥ DC
   (b) FE ⊥ E1, E1 ⊥ IH, FG ⊥ GH
   (c) OJ ⊥ JK, ON ⊥ NM
   (d) PT ⊥ TS, TS ⊥ SR, RQ ⊥ PQ

2. (a)

(b)

(c)

(d)

(e)

(f)

Exercise 4

1. (a) CD//GH   (b) MP//NO
   (c) WZ//XY, WX//ZY
   (d) SR//PQ, TP//RQ

2.

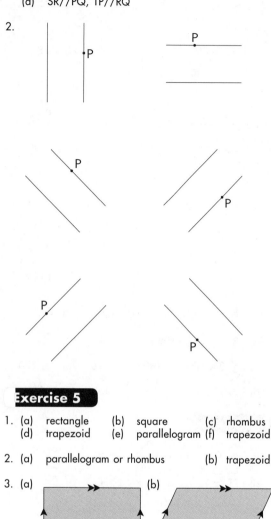

Exercise 5

1. (a) rectangle   (b) square   (c) rhombus
   (d) trapezoid   (e) parallelogram (f) trapezoid

2. (a) parallelogram or rhombus   (b) trapezoid

3. (a)   (b)

Exercise 6

1. (a) right   (b) isosceles   (c) isosceles
   (d) equilateral   (e) right   (f) equilateral

2. (a) Yes   (b) No   (c) No
   (d) No   (e) Yes

Exercise 7

1. (a) centre   (b) diameter   (c) radius

2. (a) 5   (b) 36

3. (a) Yes   (b) No   (c) No
   (d) Yes   (e) Yes

Exercise 8

1. (a) triangular prism   (b) square pyramid
   (c) triangular pyramid (d) cylinder

2. (a) 4   (b) 6   (c) 0   (d) 4

Exercise 9

1. (a) cube   (b) square pyramid
   (c) rectangular prism

2. (a)

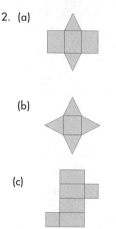

   (b)

   (c)

Unit 5 Area and Perimeter

Exercise 1

1. (a) 18 cm², 18cm   (b) 20 cm², 18cm

2. 54 cm², BC = 9 cm

3. (a) 108 cm²   (b) 448 m²   (c) $480

Exercise 2

1. (a) 4 m, 26 m   (b) 8 yd, 30 yd
   (c) 16 cm, 48 cm   (d) 13 ft, 44 ft
   (e) 15 m, 50 m

2. (a) width = 5 m, perimeter = 22 m
   (b) perimeter = 20 in.
   (c) (i) width = 3 ft   (ii) square

Exercise 3

1. (a) 134 m   (b) 90 m   (c) 72 cm

2. (a) 332 cm²   (b) 334 cm²   (c) 570 m²

3. (a) 160 m²   (b) 284 cm²   (c) 204 m²

4. (a) 90 ft²   (b) 18 yd²

Unit 6 Decimals

Exercise 1

1. (a) 0.3   (b) 0.8   (c) 3.5
   (d) 1.6   (e) 2.7   (f) 4.9

2. (a) $\frac{3}{5}$ (b) $1\frac{4}{5}$ (c) $3\frac{2}{5}$
   (d) $5\frac{3}{10}$

3. (a) 9   (b) 13   (c) 25
   (d) 86

4. (a) 6.5   (b) 3.9   (c) 52.6
   (d) 80.8

5. (a) 0.5   (b) 0.2   (c) 0.4
   (d) 2, 9, 3

6. (a) 0.9, 1.0   (b) 1.5, 2

Exercise 2

1. (a) 0.05   (b) 0.08   (c) 0.39
   (d) 0.63   (e) 10.99   (f) 9.56

2. (a) hundredths, 9 hundredths
   (b) tenths, 6 tenths

3. (a) 29.03   (b) 62.51

4. (a) 0.08   (b) 0.07
   (c) 0.4   (d) 0.1, 0.01

5. (a) 5   (b) 36   (c) 70
   (d) 100   (e) 180

6. (a) 0.15, 0.1   (b) 1.25, 1

7. (a) $\frac{1}{4}$ (b) $3\frac{3}{4}$ (c) $\frac{3}{50}$
   (d) $4\frac{1}{50}$ (e) $\frac{7}{20}$ (f) $8\frac{9}{20}$

8. (a) 0.2   (b) 5.5   (c) 10.4
   (d) 0.25   (e) 0.75   (f) 2.75
   (g) 0.95   (h) 4.48

9. (a) $2.17   (b) $5.25   (c) $10.80
   (d) $195.65

10. (a) 20.70   (b) 368.81   (c) 1042.64
    (d) 21,762.98

Exercise 3

1. (a) 0.007   (b) 0.015   (c) 0.023
   (d) 0.107   (e) 0.135   (f) 2.003
   (g) 9.005   (h) 30.018

2. (a) thousandths, 8 thousandths
   (b) thousandths, 3 thousandths

3. (a) 0.002   (b) 0.006   (c) 0.007

4. (a) 7   (b) 39   (c) 1000

5. (a) 12.001   (b) 8.025   (c) 25.403
   (d) 7.068   (e) 0.002   (f) 0.038
   (g) 0.705   (h) 6.006   (i) 90.009
   (j) 200.305

6. (a) 0.95   (b) 0.736   (c) 6.999
   (d) 0.86

7. (a) 5   (b) 4.01   (c) 2.2
   (d) 6.1

8. (a) 30   (b) 59.68   (c) 83.91
   (d) 62.291   (e) 76.99   (f) 28.83
   (g) 19.991   (h) 30.099   (i) 0.999
   (j) 6

Exercise 4

1. (a) 6   (b) 12   (c) 29
   (d) 61

2. (a) 58.9   (b) 34.4   (c) 399.6
   (d) 205.1   (e) $15.30   (f) $65.7

3. (a) 69.05   (b) 86.54   (c) 35.69
   (d) 164.57   (e) 561.96   (f) 216.24

4. (a) 37 kg   (b) 59 kg

5. (a) 22 yd   (b) 92 yd

6. (a) 5 ℓ (b) 17 ℓ

7. (a) 64 km   (b) 530 km

8. 35.38 kg

Unit 7 The Four Operations of Decimals

Exercise 1

1. (a) 1   (b) 1.5   (c) 4
   (d) 6.3   (e) 8.7   (f) 10.5
   (g) 36   (h) 31.6   (i) 49
   (j) 366.1   (k) 286.2   (l) 301.4
   (m) 8.5   (n) 4.26   (o) 6
   (p) 23.24   (q) 5.25   (r) 2.54
   (s) 24.2   (t) 59.14   (u) 91.26
   (v) 46.98   (w) 110.65   (x) 370.06

2. (a) 0.9   (b) 1.8   (c) 0.8
   (d) 3.6   (e) 4.5   (f) 7.9
   (g) 0.5   (h) 27.2   (i) 69.9
   (j) 4.8   (k) 0.23   (l) 60.3

3. (a) $9.55   (b) 5 cm taller   (c) 57.15 kg
   (d) $35.50   (e) 76.65 km   (f) 11.3 m

Exercise 2

1. (a) 6.3   (b) 4.2   (c) 0.36
   (d) 0.42

2. (a) 20.1   (b) 185.4   (c) 103
   (d) 504.72

3. (a) $1.80   (b) $1.40   (c) $6.50
(d) $17.40

4. (a) $1.65   (b) $9   (c) $25.90
(d) $36.45   (e) $61.20   (f) $92

5. (a) $13.95   (b) $3.85   (c) $13.75
(d) $76.75   (e) $27.65

Exercise 3

1. (a) 0.17   (b) 0.12   (c) 0.12
(d) 0.18   (e) 0.35   (f) 2.8
(g) 2.1   (h) 12.2   (i) 4.5
(j) 8.6

2. (a) 2.52   (b) 1.69   (c) 5.63
(d) 7.58

3. (a) 0.75   (b) 1.46   (c) 6.35
(d) 8.5

4. (a) 3.1   (b) 5.8   (c) 6.9
(d) 6.8   (e) 8.1   (f) 2.7
(g) 4.3   (h) 30.8

5. (a) $0.45   (b) $2.20   (c) $2.05

6. (a) $0.45   (b) $0.25   (c) $17.25
(d) 2.34 yd   (e) 2.1 ℓ   (f) $5.85

Unit 8 Congruent and Symmetric Figures

Exercise 1

1. (a)

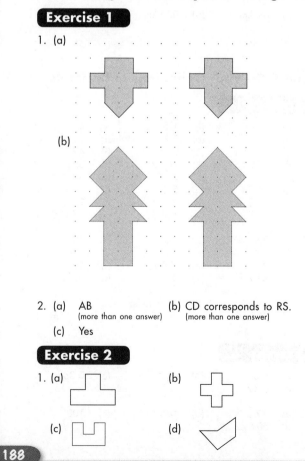

(b)

2. (a) AB
(more than one answer)
(b) CD corresponds to RS.
(more than one answer)
(c) Yes

Exercise 2

1. (a)   (b)

(c)   (d)

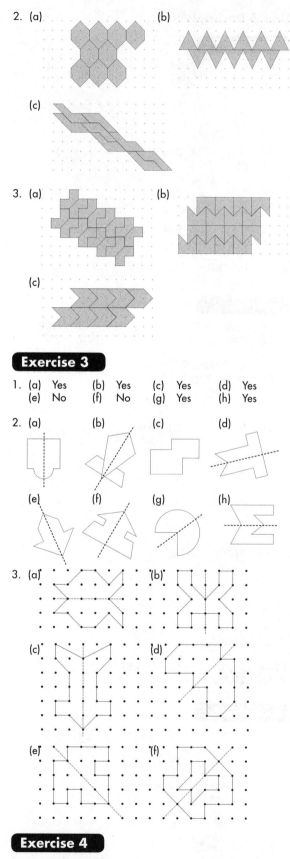

2. (a)   (b)

(c)

3. (a)   (b)

(c)

Exercise 3

1. (a) Yes   (b) Yes   (c) Yes   (d) Yes
(e) No   (f) No   (g) Yes   (h) Yes

2. (a)   (b)   (c)   (d)

(e)   (f)   (g)   (h)

3. (a)   (b)

(c)   (d)

(e)   (f)

Exercise 4

1. (a), (b), (c), (e), (f), (g)

Unit 9 Coordinate Graphs and Changes in Quantities

1. (a) (4, 6)　　(b) (7, 4)　　(c) (3, 2)
　　(d) (10, 8)　(e) (2, 8)　　(f) (11, 1)
2. (a) 3　　　　(b) 4　　　　(c) 5
　　(d) 4　　　　(e) 8

Exercise 2

1. (a) 3　　　　　(b) 4　　　　　　　(c) 7

2. (a)

Number of cakes	2	4	6	8	10
Total cost of cakes in dollars	10	20	30	40	50

(b)

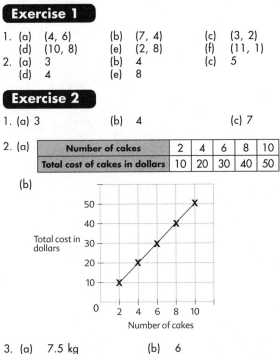

Total cost in dollars vs Number of cakes

3. (a) 7.5 kg　　　　　(b) 6

Unit 10 Data Analysis and Probability

Exercise 1

1. (a) 3　　　　(b) 4　　　　(c) 30
2. (a)

Number of children in a family

(b) 4

Exercise 2

1. (a) 6　　　　(b) 4　　　　(c) 17
2. (a) 5, 15　　(b) $\frac{1}{3}$　　(c) $\frac{2}{3}$

Exercise 3

1. 9
2.

Number that appears on die on 1st toss — Number that appears on die on 2nd toss — Outcomes

4 — 6 → 10
5 — 5 → 10
5
　6 → 11
　4 → 10
6
　5 → 11
　6 → 12

Exercise 4

1. (a) 1550　　(b) 2300　　(c) 250
　　(d) $5330
2. $2240
3. (a) $1550　　(b) $5400

Exercise 5

1. (a) Sunday　　(b) 10 hot dogs
2. (a) $60　　(b) $200　　(c) 8

Unit 11 Measures and Volume

Exercise 1

1. (a) 8 kg 300 g　　(b) 18 lb 10 oz
　　(c) 15 kg 800 g　(d) 29 gal 2 qt

2. (a) 49 ft 4 in.　　(b) 36 min 7 s
　　(c) 13 gal 3 qt　(d) 4 lb 10 oz
　　(e) 4　　　　　　(f) 8

3. (a) 2.5 kg or $2\frac{1}{2}$ kg　(b) 3 ℓ 850 ml

Exercise 2

1. (a) 39 km 200 m　(b) 55 yd
　　(c) 102 ℓ　　　(d) 33 h 18 min

2. (a) $364　　(b) 1312 m　　(c) 79 kg 50 g
　　(d) 19 gal　(e) 11 h 5 min　(f) 9 ft
　　(g) 6 m 90 cm

Exercise 3

1. (a) 2 m 12 cm　(b) 2 ft 1 in.　(c) 3 qt
　　(d) 4 years 3 mths

2. (a) 1 m 8 cm　(b) $11,232　(c) 615 g
　　(d) 12 days　(e) 5 ℓ 500 ml　(f) 3 gal 2 qt

Exercise 4

1. (a) 5　　　　(b) 9　　　　(c) 12
2. (a) 18 cm³　(b) 20 cm³　(c) 2

Exercise 5

1. (a) Length = 3 cm, Width = 3 cm, Height = 2 cm,
　　　Volume = 18 cm³

　(b) Length = 4 cm, Width = 3 cm, Height = 2 cm,
　　　Volume = 24 cm³

2. (a) 40 cm³　(b) 210 cm³　(c) 270 cm³
　　(d) 200 m³　(e) 96 m³

Blank

Blank

Blank

Blank

Blank